Course **Biology 1090, Human Biology**
Salt Lake Community College
Taking Sides readings

http://create.mcgraw-hill.com

ISBN-10: 1121524788   ISBN-13: 9781121524781

Contents

Credits

ISSUE 3

Does Direct-to-Consumer Drug Advertising Enhance Patient Choice?

YES: Paul Antony, from "Testimony Before the Senate Special Committee on Aging, United States Senate" (September 29, 2005)

NO: David A. Kessler and Douglas A. Levy, from "Direct-to-Consumer Advertising: Is It Too Late to Manage the Risks?" *Annals of Family Medicine* (January/February 2007)

ISSUE SUMMARY

YES: Paul Antony, Chief Medical Officer of Pharmaceutical Research and Manufacturers of America (PhRMA), asserts that direct-to-consumer advertising can be a powerful tool in educating millions of people and improving their health through better communication with physicians, better adherence to medication regimens, and more active involvement in their own health care.

NO: Physicians David A. Kessler and Douglas A. Levy contend that as a result of direct-to-consumer advertising, consumers ultimately take medicines they may not need, spend money on brand medicines that may be no better than alternatives, or avoid healthy behaviors.

Most uses of the term *ethical* describe a person, an action, a policy, a belief, or a theory, not a product. Yet in 1976, the Subcommittee on Health and the Environment of the U.S. House of Representatives in its "Discursive Dictionary of Health Care" defined *ethical drug* as "a *drug* which is advertised only to physicians and other *prescribing* health *professionals*. Drug manufacturers which make only or primarily such drugs are referred to as the ethical drug industry. Synonymous with *prescription drug*" (italics in original).

Less than a decade later, pharmaceutical companies began advertising directly to consumers, and now one seldom hears the term *ethical drug*. Manufacturers still advertise to physicians, and physicians must still prescribe the drugs, but consumers are now a prime marketing target, especially through television. In 1983, the Food and Drug Administration (FDA), which regulates the approval and marketing of medications, imposed a moratorium on this type of marketing but lifted it two years later. In 1997, the agency changed its guidelines to allow more flexibility in television advertising in describing medication risks.

As any television viewer or magazine reader knows, the amount and intensity of drug advertising has been escalating ever since. In its November 2006 report, "Prescription Drugs: Improvements Needed in FDA's Oversight of Direct-to-Consumer Advertising," the General Accounting Office (GAO) of the U.S. House of Representatives reported that drug company spending on prescription drugs increased twice as fast from 1997 through 2005 as spending on promotion to physicians or on research and development. The FDA reviews only a small portion of the direct-to-consumer material it receives, is issuing fewer regulatory letters than it did in a 2002 GAO study, and is taking longer to issue them. The GAO concluded that the agency "cannot ensure that it is identifying or reviewing those materials that it would consider to be of the highest priority."

According to a content analysis of drug advertising in magazines from 1989 through 1998, conducted by Michael Wilkes and his colleagues at the University of California at Los Angeles, the most common medical conditions in these ads were allergies, obstetrical/gynecological, dermatological, cardiovascular, HIV/AIDS, and tobacco addiction. Women were more likely to be targeted than men.

The ads worked. The GAO report found that between 1999 and 2000 the number of prescriptions dispensed for the most heavily advertised drugs rose 25 percent but increased only 4 percent for not-so-visibly promoted drugs. Nicotine patches for tobacco addiction became an $800 million business as a result of advertising. Aggressive marketing of Claritin, produced by Schering-Plough, resulted in this drug accounting for more than half of the $1.8 billion spent in its marketing category. (In November 2002, the FDA took Claritin off the prescription drug list so that it is now available over the counter.)

A national survey conducted by *Prevention Magazine* in 1998 found that more than 53 million consumers talked to their physicians about an advertised medication, and another 49 million looked for information from another source, such as an Internet site. The GAO report estimates that about 8.5 million consumers (5 percent of the total) have both requested and received a prescription for a particular drug as a result of seeing a direct-to-consumer ad.

Although studies have found that consumers remember drug advertising, the consumers have misconceptions about a government's role in regulating this practice. Half of the respondents in a Sacramento County survey conducted by Wilkes and his UCLA colleagues believed that drug ads had to be submitted to the government for prior approval, which is not the case. Nor is it true, as 43 percent believed, that only completely safe drugs can be advertised or that drugs with serious side effects cannot be advertised, as 22 percent believed. Drug manufacturers are only required to truthfully present a fair balance of risks and effectiveness.

On balance, is direct-to-consumer advertising ethically justified or not? Does it enhance patient autonomy by giving information that in earlier decades was available only to physicians? The following selections provide two views of the debate. From an industry standpoint, Paul Antony finds benefits to individual health from alerting consumers to treatable conditions and encouraging them to take their medicines as prescribed. From their perspectives as physicians, David A. Kessler and Douglas A. Levy question whether industry spending on direct-to-consumer advertising is for patient benefit and may in fact lead to unnecessary and risky choices.

YES ↵   **Paul Antony**

Testimony Before the Senate Special Committee on Aging

Mr. Chairman, Ranking Member Kohl and Members of the Committee, on behalf of the Pharmaceutical Research and Manufacturers of America (PhRMA), I am pleased to appear at this hearing today on direct-to-consumer (DTC) advertising. I am Paul Antony, M.D., Chief Medical Officer at PhRMA.

DTC advertising has been proven to be beneficial to American patients. And, continuing regulatory oversight by the FDA helps ensure that the content of DTC advertising informs and educates consumers about medical conditions and treatment options. PhRMA and its member companies have a responsibility to ensure that ads comply with FDA regulations. We take that job seriously. We want to continue to be a valuable contributor to improving public health.

DTC advertising can be a powerful tool in educating millions of people and improving health. Because of DTC advertising, large numbers of Americans are prompted to discuss illnesses with their doctors for the first time. Because of DTC advertising, patients become more involved in their own health care decisions, and are proactive in their patient–doctor dialogue. Because of DTC advertising, patients are more likely to take their prescribed medicines.

PhRMA's Guiding Principles on Direct-to-Consumer Advertisements about Prescription Medicines

PhRMA and its member companies have long understood the special relationship we have with the patients that use our innovative medicines. Despite the very positive role DTC advertising plays in educating patients about health issues and options, over the years, we have heard the concerns expressed about DTC advertising—that some ads may oversell benefits and undersell risks; that some ads may lead to inappropriate prescribing; that some patients may not be able to afford the advertised medicines; and that some ads may not be appropriate for some audiences. Some doctors have also complained that drug companies launch advertising campaigns without helping to educate doctors in advance. Although actual practice and data on the effects of DTC advertising differ from these concerns, PhRMA recognized our obligation to act. On July 29,

YES / Paul Antony   **47**

2005, PhRMA's Board of Directors unanimously approved Guiding Principles on Direct-to-Consumer Advertisements About Prescription Medicine. These principles help ensure that DTC advertising remains an important and powerful tool to educate patients while at the same time addressing many of the concerns expressed about DTC advertising over the past few years.

First, PhRMA member companies take their responsibility to fully comply with FDA advertising regulations very seriously. Our advertising is already required to be accurate and not misleading; it can only make claims supported by substantial evidence; it must reflect the balance between risks and benefits; and it must be consistent with FDA-approved labeling. However, patients, health care providers and the general public expect us to do more than just meet our exacting legal obligations, and our Guiding Principles do go further.

Our principles recognize that at the heart of our companies' DTC communications efforts is patient education. This means that DTC communications designed to market a medicine should responsibly educate patients about a medicine, including the conditions for which it may be prescribed. DTC advertising should also foster responsible communications between patients and health care professionals to help the patient achieve better health and a better appreciation of a medicine's known benefits and risks. Specifically, the Principles state that risk and safety information should be designed to achieve a balanced presentation of both risks and benefits associated with the advertised medicines.

Our Guiding Principles recognize that companies should spend appropriate time educating health care professionals about a new medicine before it is advertised to patients. That way, providers will be prepared to discuss the appropriateness of a given medication with a patient.

Current law provides that companies must submit their DTC television advertisements to FDA upon first use for FDA's review at its discretion. Companies that sign onto these Guiding Principles agree to submit all new DTC television ads to the FDA before releasing these ads for broadcast, giving the agency an opportunity to review consistent with its priorities and resources. Companies also commit to informing FDA of the earliest date the advertisement is set to air. Should new information concerning a previously unknown safety risk be discovered, companies commit to work with FDA to "responsibly alter or discontinue a DTC advertising campaign."

In addition, the Principles encourage companies to include, where feasible, information about help for the uninsured and underinsured in their DTC communications. Our member companies offer a host of programs that can assist needy patients with their medicines.

The Principles also recognize that ads should respect the seriousness of the health condition and medicine being advertised and that ads employing humor or entertainment may not be appropriate in all instances.

As a result of concerns that certain prescription drug ads may not be suitable for all viewing audiences, the Guiding Principles state that, "DTC television and print advertisements should be targeted to avoid audiences that are not age appropriate for the messages involved."

Signatory companies are committed to establishing their own internal processes to ensure compliance with the Guiding Principles and to broadly disseminate them internally and to advertisers. In addition, PhRMA's Board unanimously approved the creation of an office of accountability to ensure the public has an opportunity to comment on companies' compliance with these Principles. The office of accountability will be responsible for receiving comments from the general public and from health care professionals regarding DTC ads by any company that publicly states it will follow the principles. The PhRMA office of accountability will provide to these companies any comment that is reasonably related to compliance with the Principles. Periodic reports will be issued by the PhRMA office of accountability to the public regarding the nature of the comments. Each report will also be submitted to the FDA.

PhRMA's Board also agreed to select an independent panel of outside experts and individuals to review reports from the office of accountability after one year and evaluate overall trends in the industry as they relate to the Principles. The panel will be empowered to make recommendations in accordance with the Principles. The Principles will go into effect in January 2006.

We believe these Principles will help patients and health care professionals get the information they need to make informed health care decisions.

The Value of DTC Advertising
Informing and Empowering Consumers

Surveys indicate that DTC advertising makes consumers aware of new drugs and their benefits, as well as risks and side effects with the drugs advertised. They help consumers recognize symptoms and seek appropriate care. According to an article in *The New England Journal of Medicine*, DTC advertising is concentrated among a few therapeutic categories. These are therapeutic categories in which consumers can recognize their own symptoms, such as arthritis, seasonal allergies, and obesity; or for pharmaceuticals that treat chronic diseases with many undiagnosed sufferers, such as high cholesterol, osteoporosis, and depression.

DTC advertising gets patients talking to their doctors about conditions that may otherwise have gone undiagnosed or undertreated. For example, a study conducted by RAND Health and published in *The New England Journal of Medicine* found that nearly half of all adults in the United States fail to receive recommended health care. According to researchers on the RAND study, "the deficiencies in care . . . pose serious threats to the health of the American public that could contribute to thousands of preventable deaths in the United States each year." The study found underuse of prescription medications in seven of the nine conditions for which prescription medicines were the recommended treatment. Conditions for which underuse was found include asthma, cerebrovascular disease, congestive heart failure, diabetes, hip fracture, hyperlipidemia and hypertension. Of those seven conditions for which RAND found underuse of recommended prescription medicines, five are DTC advertised.

YES / Paul Antony   **49**

The Rand Study, as well as other studies, highlight the underuse of needed medications and other healthcare services in the U.S.

- According to a nationally representative study of 9,090 people aged 18 and up, published in *JAMA*, about 43 percent of participants with recent major depression are getting inadequate therapy.
- A 2004 study published in the *Archives of Internal Medicine*, found that, "In older patients, failures to prescribe indicated medications, monitor medications appropriately, document necessary information, educate patients, and maintain continuity are more common prescribing problems than is use of inappropriate drugs."
- A May/June 2003 study published in the *Journal of Managed Care Pharmacy*, which examined claims data from 3 of the 10 largest health plans in California to determine the appropriateness of prescription medication use based upon widely accepted treatment guidelines, found that "effective medication appears to be underused." Of the four therapeutic areas of study—asthma, CHF, depression, and common cold or upper respiratory tract infections—asthma, CHF, and depression were undertreated. The researchers concluded that "the results are particularly surprising and disturbing when we take into account the fact that three of the conditions studied (asthma, CHF, and depression) are known to produce high costs to the healthcare system."
- According to a study released in May 2005 by the Stanford University School of Medicine, among patients with high cholesterol in moderate and high-risk groups, researchers found fewer than half of patient visits ended with a statin recommendation. Based on the findings, the researchers say physicians should be more aggressive in investigating statin therapy for patients with a high or moderate risk of heart disease, and that patients should ask for their cholesterol levels to be checked regularly.

Increasing Communication between the Doctor and Patient

A vast majority of patients (93 percent) who asked about a drug reported that their doctor "welcomed the questions." Of patients who asked about a drug, 77 percent reported that their relationship with their doctor remained unchanged as a result of the office visit, and 20 percent reported that their relationship improved. In addition, both an FDA survey of physicians (from a random sample of 500 physicians from the American Medical Association's database) and a survey by the nation's oldest and largest African-American medical association, found that DTC advertisements raise disease awareness and bolster doctor–patient ties.

The doctor–patient relationship is enhanced if DTC advertising prompts a patient to talk to his doctor for the first time about a previously undiscussed condition, to comply with a prescribed treatment regimen, or to become aware of a risk or side effect that was otherwise unknown. A 2002 *Prevention Magazine* survey found that 24.8 million Americans spoke with their doctor about a medical condition for the first time as a result of seeing a DTC advertisement.

50   ISSUE 3 / Does Direct-to-Consumer Drug Advertising Enhance . . . ?

Similarly, the FDA patient survey on DTC advertising found that nearly one in five patients reported speaking to a physician about a condition for the first time because of a DTC ad.

PhRMA and its member companies believe it is vital that patients, in consultation with their doctors, make decisions about treatments and medicines. Prescribing decisions should be dominated by the doctor's advice. While our member companies direct a large majority of their promotional activities toward physicians, such promotion in no way guarantees medicines will be prescribed.

According to a General Accounting Office report, of the 61.1 million people (33 percent of adults) who had discussions with their physician as a result of a DTC advertisement in 2001, only 8.5 million (5 percent of adults) actually received a prescription for the product, a small percentage of the total volume of prescriptions dispensed. Indeed, an FDA survey of physicians revealed that the vast majority of physicians do not feel pressure to prescribe. According to the survey, 91 percent of physicians said that their patients did not try to influence treatment courses in a way that would have been harmful and 72 percent of physicians, when asked for prescription for a specific brand name drug, felt little or no pressure to prescribe a medicine.

De-stigmatizing Disease

DTC advertising also encourages patients to discuss medical problems that otherwise may not have been discussed because it was either thought to be too personal or that there was a stigma attached to the disease. For example, a Health Affairs article examined the value of innovation and noted that depression medications, known as selective serotonin reuptake inhibitors (SSRIs), that have been DTC advertised, have led to significant treatment expansion. Prior to the 1990s, it was estimated that about half of those persons who met a clinical definition of depression were not appropriately diagnosed, and many of those diagnosed did not receive clinically appropriate treatment. However, in the 1990s with the advent of SSRIs, treatment has been expanded. According to the article, "Manufacturers of SSRIs encouraged doctors to watch for depression and the reduced stigma afforded by the new medications induced patients to seek help." As a result, diagnosis and treatment for depression doubled over the 1990s.

Utilization and DTC Advertising

According to reports and studies, there is no direct relationship between DTC advertising and the price growth of drugs. For example, in comments to the FDA in December 2003, the FTC stated, "[DTC advertising] can empower consumers to manage their own health care by providing information that will help them, with the assistance of their doctors, to make better informed decisions about their treatment options. . . . Consumer receive these benefits from DTC advertising with little, if any, evidence that such advertising increases prescription drug prices." Notably, since January 2000, the CPI component that tracks prescription medicines have been in line with overall medical inflation.

YES / Paul Antony **51**

The FTC comments referenced above also note, "DTC advertising accounts for a relatively small proportion of the total cost of drugs, which reinforces the view that such advertising would have a limited, if any, effect on price." Likewise, a study by Harvard University and the Massachusetts Institute of Technology and published by the Kaiser Family Foundation found that DTC advertising accounts for less than 2 percent of the total U.S. spending for prescription medicines.

One study in *The American Journal of Managed Care* looked at whether pharmaceutical marketing has led to an increase in the use of medications by patients with marginal indications. The study found that high-risk individuals were receiving lipid-lowering treatment "consistent with evidence-based practice guidelines" despite the fact that "a substantial portion of patients continue to remain untreated and undertreated. . . ." The study concluded that "greater overall use did not appear to be associated with a shift towards patients with less CV [cardiovascular] risk."

Pharmaceutical utilization is increasing for reasons other than DTC advertising. As the June 2003 study of DTC advertising commissioned by the Kaiser Family Foundation found, "[O]ur estimates indicate that DTCA is important, but not the primary driver of recent growth [in prescription drug spending]."

Other reasons pharmaceutical utilization is increasing, include:

- Improved Medicines—Many new medicines replace higher-cost surgeries and hospital care. In 2004 alone, pharmaceutical companies added 38 new medicines and over the last decade, over 300 new medicines have become available for treating patients. These include important new medicines for some of the most devastating and costly diseases, including: AIDS, cancer, heart disease, Alzheimer's, and diabetes. According to a study prepared for the Department of Health and Human Services, "[n]ew medications are not simply more costly than older ones. They may be more effective or have fewer side effects; some may treat conditions for which no treatment was available."
- New Standards of Medical Practice Encouraging Greater Use of Pharmaceuticals—Clinical standards are changing to emphasize earlier and tighter control of a range of conditions, such as diabetes, hypertension and cardiovascular disease. For example, new recommendations from the two provider groups suggest that early treatment, including lifestyle changes and treatment with two or more types of medications, can significantly reduce the risk of later complications and improve the quality of life for people with type 2 diabetes.
- Greater Treatment of Previously Undiagnosed and Untreated Conditions—According to guidelines developed by the National Heart, Lung, and Blood Institute's National Cholesterol Education Program (NCEP) Adult Treatment Panel (ATP), approximately 36 million adults should be taking medicines to lower their cholesterol, a number that has grown from 13 million just 8 years ago.
- Aging of America—The aging of American translates into greater reliance on pharmaceuticals. For example, congestive heart failure affects an estimated 2 percent of Americans age 40 to 59, more than 5 percent of those aged 60 to 69, and 10 percent of those 70 or more.

52   ISSUE 3 / Does Direct-to-Consumer Drug Advertising Enhance . . . ?

While some assume that DTC advertising leads to increased use of newer medicines rather than generic medicines, generics represent just over 50 percent of all prescriptions (generics are historically not DTC advertised). In contrast, in Europe, where DTC advertising is prohibited, the percentage of prescriptions that are generic is significantly lower. Likewise, it is worth noting that while broadcast DTC has been in place since 1997, the rate of growth in drug cost increases has declined in each of the last 5 years and in 2004 was below the rate of growth in overall health care costs.

Economic Value of DTC Advertising

Increased spending on pharmaceuticals often leads to lower spending on other forms of more costly health care. New drugs are the most heavily advertised drugs, a point critics often emphasize. However, the use of newer drugs tends to lower all types of non-drug medical spending, resulting in a net reduction in the total cost of treating a condition. For example, on average replacing an older drug with a drug 15 years newer increases spending on drugs by $18, but reduces overall costs by $111.

The Tufts Center for the Study of Drug Development reports that disease management organizations surveyed believe that increased spending on prescription drugs reduces hospital inpatient costs. "Since prescription drugs account for less than 10 percent of total current U.S. health care spending, while inpatient care accounts for 32 percent, the increased use of appropriate pharmaceutical therapies may help moderate or reduce growth in the costliest component of the U.S. health care system," according to Tufts Center Director Kenneth I. Kaitin.

Opponents also compare the amount of money spent by drug companies on marketing and advertising to the amount they spend on research and development of new drugs. However, in 2004, pharmaceutical manufacturers spent an estimated $4.15 billion on DTC advertising, according to IMS Health, compared to $49.3 billion in total R&D spending by the biopharmaceutical industry, according to Burrill & Company. PhRMA members alone spent $38.8 billion on R&D in 2004.

Conclusion

DTC advertising provides value to patients by making them aware of risks and benefits of new drugs; it empowers patients and enhances the public health; it plays a vital role in addressing a major problem in this country of under-treatment and underdiagnosis of disease; it encourages patients to discuss medical problems with their health care provider that may otherwise not be discussed due to a stigma being attached to the disease; and it encourages patient compliance with physician-directed treatment regimens.

Given the progress that continues to be made in society's battle against disease, patients are seeking more information about medical problems and potential treatments. The purpose of DTC advertising is to foster an informed conversation about health, disease and treatments between patients and their

YES / Paul Antony   **53**

health care practitioners. Our Guiding Principles are an important step in ensuring patients and health care professionals get the information they need to make informed health care decisions.

This concludes my written testimony. I would be happy to answer any questions or to supply any additional material by Members or Committee Staff on this or any other issue.

**David A. Kessler and
Douglas A. Levy**

 **NO**

Direct-to-Consumer Advertising: Is It Too Late to Manage the Risks?

Pharmaceutical spending on television commercials nearly doubled from $654 million in 2001 to a staggering $1.19 billion in 2005. Nearly one third of the 2005 spending was on only 1 category: sleep medicines.[1] Yet, sleep disorders, however problematic and serious they may be, are almost inconsequential when compared with the major causes of the death in the United States: cardiovascular disease, cancer, and unintentional injuries.[2] No matter how much the industry claims its advertising provides public health benefits, the amount spent promoting drugs for conditions of varying severity begs the question of whether the industry truly is acting for the public benefit.

As Frosch et al. show in this issue,[3] nearly all pharmaceutical ads are based on emotional appeals, not facts, and few provide necessary details about the causes of a medical condition, risk factors, or lifestyle changes that may be appropriate alternatives to pharmaceutical intervention.

Although none of these findings are surprising, they should be disturbing.

As physicians, we know that even the most effective pharmaceutical may not be right for every patient. Physicians consider everything from individual risk factors and medical history to lifestyle and insurance status before writing a prescription. Yet, when patients walk in the door having just seen a television ad showing a miserable allergy sufferer dancing through a weed-filled field, they expect that a simple stroke of a pen onto a prescription pad will solve whatever their problems may be. Patients learn for the first time about conditions they never worried about before and ask physicians for new medicines by trade name because they saw it on television.

Patients have always expected simple answers to complex questions, but direct-to-consumer (DTC) advertising has elevated this problem to new heights, because patients in some ways now rely on Madison Avenue as a provider of health information. There is nothing wrong with pharmaceutical companies communicating directly with consumers, but they should adhere to the standards and ethics of medicine, not the standards and ethics of selling soap or some other consumer product that presents minimal risks.

Pharmaceutical companies like to say that DTC ads make people aware of medical conditions they did not know they had. Industry spokesman Paul Antony told a Senate hearing in 2005, "DTC advertising can be a powerful tool in educating millions of people and improving health."[4]

NO / Kessler and Levy   **55**

Even if health education is true theoretically, it does not appear to be true in practice. Furthermore, one might question the societal benefit should such communications result in millions more people with conditions being diagnosed that are not major factors in morbidity and mortality. There likely would be strong support for pharmaceutical advertising if it led to millions more conditions diagnosed and people being treated for diabetes or heart disease.

What is equally important is the possibility—the likelihood—that consumers who make health decisions based on what they learn from television commercials ultimately take medicines they may not need, spend money on brand medicines that may be no better than alternatives, or avoid healthy behaviors because they falsely think a medicine is all they need.

In general, the ads that consumers see do not contain the right balance of information to provide any meaningful health education. The facts gleaned from DTC ads are minimal at best, which is an unsurprising consequence of condensing decades of research into a 60-second commercial. Moreover, findings from patients' and physicians' surveys show that the messages that patients take from DTC ads and into their physicians' offices are often wrong.[5] The pharmaceutical companies have done a skillful job of portraying complex medicines in the simplest terms—even if doing so creates inaccurate perceptions in the minds of our patients.

One fact is unquestionable: DTC ads do not effectively or consistently convey important information about product risks and benefits. When the Food and Drug Administration surveyed a sampling of primary care and specialty physicians in 2002, 41% of all physicians said they believed their patients were confused about a drug's efficacy because of DTC ads they saw; 22% of primary care physicians and 13% of specialists said they felt "somewhat" or "very" pressured to prescribe a drug when a patient requested it.[6] Even if physicians resist this pressure, the possibility of risk remains.

Under increased scrutiny, major pharmaceutical companies last year announced new advertising guidelines and pledged to portray serious health conditions seriously and to disclose risks, side effects, and warnings adequately.[7] Although these efforts may be a step in the right direction, physicians, consumers, and policy makers must take further action so that the facts about medicines are not lost in the advertising fog. As Frosch et al. correctly point out, the consequences of poor judgments are quite different for drugs than they are for soap.

References

1. Prescription drugs. *Media Week.* May 1, 2006;SR30.

2. *Health, United States, 2005 With Chartbook on Trends in the Health of Americans.* Hyattsville, Md: National Center for Health Statistics; 2005:195.

3. Frosch DL, Krueger PM, Hornik RC, Cronholm PF, Barg FK. Creating demand for prescription drugs: a content analysis of television direct-to-consumer advertising. *Ann Fam Med.* 2007;5(1):6–13.

4. PhRMA Chief Medical Officer Testifies on DTC Advertising. Washington, DC; 2005: News release publishing PhRMA testimony at Senate hearing. . . .

56   ISSUE 3 / Does Direct-to-Consumer Drug Advertising Enhance . . . ?

5. Aikin KJ, Braman AC. Patient and Physician Attitudes and Behaviors Associated With DTC Promotion of Prescription Drugs—Summary of FDA Survey Research Results. Washington, DC: US Department of Health and Human Services. Food and Drug Administration. Center for Drug Evaluation and Research; 2004:63–84.

6. *The Impact of Direct-to-Consumer Drug Advertising on Seniors' Health and Health Care Costs. Senate Special Committee on Aging.* First Session ed. Washington, DC: US Government Printing Office; 2005:30.

7. PhRMA guiding principles direct-to-consumer advertisements about prescription medicines. 2005. . . .

POSTSCRIPT

Does Direct-to-Consumer Drug Advertising Enhance Patient Choice?

From 1996 to 2005, spending on direct-to-consumer advertising increased by 330 percent but still made up only 14 percent of the total promotional spending. Most drug advertising still targets physicians. The number of letters the FDA sent to pharmaceutical manufacturers about violations in their advertising fell from 142 in 1997 to only 21 in 2006 (Julie M. Donohue et al., "A Decade of Direct-to-Consumer Advertising of Prescription Drugs," *New England Journal of Medicine,* August 16, 2007).

Americans watch on average 16 hours of prescription drug advertising a year. A content analysis of these ads found limited information about the causes of a disease or who might be at risk. The ads appeal to the emotional aspect of losing control over some life activities and minimize lifestyle changes as a way to regain control (Dominick L. Frosch et al., "Creating Demand for Prescription Drugs: A Content Analysis of Television Direct-to-Consumer Advertising," *Annals of Family Medicine,* January/February 2007).

Researchers from Harvard University/Massachusetts General Hospital and Harris Interactive conducted a national telephone survey of consumers in 2002 asking about their experience with direct-to-consumer drug advertising. About 35 percent reported that an ad prompted them to have a discussion with a physician about the drug or the condition. A quarter of these patients received a new diagnosis, and nearly three-quarters were given a prescription, with about 43 percent getting a prescription for the advertised drug. About four out of five consumers who got a drug and took it as prescribed reported feeling much or somewhat better (Joel S. Weissman et al., "Consumers' Reports on the Health Effects of Direct-to-Consumer Drug Advertising," *Health Affairs*, February 2003). The same team also surveyed physicians on this issue. They pointed to improved communication and education as a benefit of direct-to-consumer advertising but also felt it led patients to seek unnecessary treatments. When the advertised drug was prescribed, 46 percent of physicians said it was the most effective treatment and 48 percent said that other drugs were equally effective. Among the most common new diagnoses were impotence (15.5 percent), anxiety (9 percent), and arthritis (6.8 percent) (Joel Weissman et al., "Physicians Report on Patient Encounters Involving Direct-to-Consumer Advertising," *Health Affairs*, April 28, 2004).

A more subtle form of consumer persuasion involves news reporting on medication studies, which often fail to report pharmaceutical funding and frequently refer to medications by their brand names instead of their generic counterparts. Since favorable studies get the most press, consumers are indirectly encouraged to ask their physicians for the brand name drug. See Michael Hochman et al., "News Media Coverage of Medication Research," *Journal of the American Medical Association* (October 2, 2008).

Internet References . . .

Euthanasia and Physician-Assisted Suicide: All Sides of the Issues

This site offers a general overview of the controversy concerning physician-assisted suicide as well as statistics and a list of Web sites that represent both sides of the debate.

**http://www.religioustolerance.org/
euthanas.htm**

National Hospice and Palliative Care Organization

This organization's Web site has information about each state's advance directive rules as well as aspects of care of dying people.

http://www.nhpco.org

ISSUE 11

Should Vaccination for HPV Be Mandated for Teenage Girls?

YES: Joseph E. Balog, from "The Moral Justification for a Compulsory Human Papillomavirus Vaccination Program," *American Journal of Public Health* (April 2009)

NO: Gail Javitt, Deena Berkowitz, and Lawrence O. Gostin, from "Assessing Mandatory HPV Vaccination: Who Should Call the Shots?" *The Journal of Law, Medicine and Ethics* (Summer 2008)

ISSUE SUMMARY

YES: Health science professor Joseph E. Balog believes that a principle-based approach to moral reasoning leads to the conclusion that compulsory HPV vaccinations for teenage girls can be justified on moral, scientific, and public health grounds.

NO: Law professors Gail Javitt and Lawrence O. Gostin and physician Deena Berkowitz believe that, given the limited data and experience, and the fact that HPV does not pose imminent and significant risk to others, mandating HPV vaccine is premature.

Human papillomavirus (HPV) is the most common sexually transmitted infection in the United States, with about 6.2 million individuals newly infected every year. Over a quarter (26.8 percent) of females aged 14–24 have an HPV infection, and among the age group 20–24, almost half (44.8 percent) are infected. There is no treatment, but the vast majority (90 percent) of the women clear the virus within 2 years.

HPV is linked to cancer of the cervix (the narrow end of the uterus, or womb), which is the second most common cancer among women globally. (Breast cancer is the first.) Each year around the world about 493,000 cases of cervical cancer are diagnosed, and 274,000 deaths from this disease are reported. Most of these cases are among young women in their child-bearing and child-rearing years. More than 80 percent of the cases occur in developing countries, and this percentage is rising. In the United States, the incidence of cervical cancer is low, but still significant; about 11,000 new cases occur every year, leading to 3,700 deaths. The risk of death in the United States is very much lower because of the widespread use of the Papanicolaou (Pap) test, which detects cervical cancer at an early and usually treatable stage.

But for those whose infection does not go away, the consequences are serious, especially if the infection comes from the high-risk strain of HPV. The high-risk strain is present in nearly all (99 percent) of cervical cancers. Still, if a young woman is infected with the lower-risk variation, the association with cervical cancer is relatively low.

Clearly, cervical cancer related to HPV infection in the developing world is a major public health problem. But what about the United States? The chances of becoming infected with HPV are quite high, but the chances of this infection leading to cervical cancer are relatively low.

This issue was moved from the theoretical to the real world in June 2006 when the Food and Drug Administration (FDA), which must approve the safety and effectiveness of a medication or vaccine before it is introduced to the general public, licensed a prophylactic (preventive) vaccine against four strains of HPV. The vaccine protects against 70 percent of cervical cancers linked to HPV, but not against all cancer-causing types of HPV. The vaccine was approved for females aged 9–26. Commonly known as Gardasil, its trade name, the vaccine is manufactured and marketed by Merck. In October 2009, the FDA approved a second HPV vaccine, Cervarix, which targets a different HPV strain and is manufactured by GlaxoSmithKline.

The Advisory Committee on Immunization Practices of the Centers for Disease Control and Prevention (CDC) then recommended routine vaccination of 11- and 12-year-old girls with three doses of the vaccine as well as vaccination of 13- to 26-year-olds who had no opportunity to receive the vaccine when they were younger. The three-dose vaccination costs $360, making it one of the most costly vaccines available.

The CDC's recommendations were just that—recommendations. The controversy began when Merck officials lobbied state legislatures to require the vaccine as a condition of school entry for girls entering the sixth grade. By executive order from the governor, in 2007 Texas became the first state to mandate this use of the vaccine, but the state legislature passed legislation to override the executive order and the governor did not veto it. As a result of the controversy, Merck withdrew its lobbying campaign.

As of October 2010 legislators in at least 41 states and the District of Columbia have introduced legislation to require, fund, or educate the public about HPV vaccines. At least 19 states have enacted such legislation.

The following selections explore this controversy from different perspectives. After analyzing the scientific and public health grounds for compulsory HPV vaccinations for teenage girls, health science professor Joseph E. Balog concludes that it can be defended on those grounds as well as moral principles. Gail Javitt and Lawrence O. Gostin, law professors, and Deena Berkowitz, a physician, based their objections on the lack of long-term data on safety and effectiveness and on the lack of imminent risk to others posed by HPV. They believe that mandates would undermine trust in the vaccine and contribute to the prevalent fear of vaccination in general.

YES ↵

Joseph E. Balog

The Moral Justification for a Compulsory Human Papillomavirus Vaccination Program

Early in the 1950s, polio hysteria erupted across the United States in the wake of a rash of new cases. Thousands of people, mostly young children, were crippled. In 1952, more than 58,000 cases of polio were reported, including 21,000 cases of paralytic polio and more than 3000 deaths. Terrified parents, worried that polio would render their children unable to walk or force them into iron lungs,[1] kept their children away from beaches and movie theaters. Medical researchers conducted experimental studies in public schools. Polio became one of the most feared and studied diseases in the mid-20th century.[2,3]

In retrospect, the decision to implement a compulsory vaccination program for polio was an effective, legal, and ethical use of public health authority. The vaccine was effective: the incidence rate for polio was 3.6 times higher for unvaccinated than vaccinated children, the Salk vaccine was 80% to 90% successful in preventing paralytic poliomyelitis, and over the two- to three-year period after the Salk vaccine was introduced, an overall 60% to 70% prevention rate was achieved.[1,2,4] As a result, the elimination of poliomyelitis has been called one of the 10 great public health achievements of the twentieth century in the United States.[5] . . .

A compulsory HPV vaccination program also appears to be ethically permissible according to the harm principle proposed by John Stuart Mill in *On Liberty*.[6] Mill argued that "the only purpose for which power can be rightfully exercised over any member of a civilized community, against his will, is to prevent harm to others."[7] In the polio vaccination campaign, the diminution of individual autonomy and liberty was justified by the collective interest of the public in preventing harm from disease and promoting the common good. The ethical principles of beneficence and nonmaleficence and the desire to prevent harm overrode the ethical principles of autonomy and liberty. . . .

The desire of some health professionals to prevent illness and deaths from diseases that have low morbidity and mortality rates raises questions about whether the ends—lowered morbidity and mortality rates—justify the means—compulsory vaccinations. The key moral dilemma is whether a utilitarian perspective that weighs the social and health care consequences and costs should override a deontological perspective that it is always good to act

YES / Joseph E. Balog   **203**

to prevent harm, disease, and death. In other words, is the utility and good of a compulsory vaccine in preventing harm greater than the utility and good of preserving individual liberty and choice? . . .

Ethics and Morality of Compulsory Vaccination

To begin the process of moral reasoning on this dilemma, it is reasonable to acknowledge that health professionals and members of society who support a compulsory vaccination program and their counterparts who oppose compulsory vaccination programs and prefer alternatives such as voluntary vaccinations, premarital abstinence programs, improved screening and treatment, and other options, appear virtuous. None of the proposed alternatives to compulsory vaccination are intended to do harm. Rather, all parties to the debate desire good, achieved through differing means. Furthermore, neither the act of making a compulsory HPV vaccination program available nor implementing alternative programs possesses any inherent or intrinsic feature that is wrong or harmful. Therefore, from a public health perspective, a judgment about the rightness or wrongness of a compulsory vaccination program should be determined by assessing whether key ethical principles justify such action, whether this action reduces harm to individuals and society, and whether this action produces consequences that are at least as good as, if not better than, alternative actions that are available for preventing disease and death.

Beneficence and Nonmaleficence

HPV infection can lead to suffering and harm. Scientific observations have documented that young people in the United States engage in sexual practices that place them at risk for STIs and subsequent illnesses such as cervical cancer. For example, it is estimated that 46% of high school students have sexual intercourse with another person by the time they graduate and 75% of young people have sexual relationships before they marry.[7–11] STIs are reportedly common among sexually active adolescent girls. For example, the Centers for Disease Control and Prevention estimates that 3.2 million adolescent girls have STIs, and of these, 18.3% are infected with HPV. . . .

Evidence about the rates of HPV infections and sexual activity among the young, the ineffectiveness of abstinence programs, and the quantity and quality of communications between parents and children on sexual issues demonstrates a need for public health interventions that prevent the harm that HPV causes among young people. A compulsory or voluntary vaccination program could greatly improve disease prevention over the status quo. It would be wrong to uphold a symbolic ideal of no sexual intercourse among youths by prohibiting an alternative that can alleviate a real harm. In an ideal world, all people would stop engaging in risky sexual behaviors and all parents would engage in meaningful and effective discussions with their children about sexual (and other important) matters. However, these worthy ideals are not realistic enough, nor likely to occur soon and often enough, to match the effectiveness of a vaccine that is available now to eliminate real and immediate harm. Reducing the transmission of HPV infection among youths is an act of beneficence, and the alternative—opposing vaccinations that can reduce real and probable harm or simply failing to provide them—is an act of malevolence.

Autonomy

An important question is, whose autonomy should have a higher priority, the child's or the parent's? It is reasonable to consider who is at greater risk and who stands to gain a greater benefit. In the case of HPV vaccination of youths who have not yet been exposed to HPV, the right of the child to receive the preventive measure should override respect for the parents' autonomy and the parents' desire to teach social beliefs that restrict health care action, because the health threat directly involves the life of the child. The rights, autonomy, and desires of parents are important, but the consequences of the decision affect them indirectly. If respect for parental autonomy leads to denying children access to effective health care, the probability of harm and the loss of benefits are much greater for the children than for their parents.

Disease, disability, and loss of life are burdens—for both individuals and society—that outweigh the benefits derived from upholding parental rights and authority. Furthermore, the availability of a voluntary or compulsory vaccination program does not deprive parents of the opportunity, or the right, to teach their own values to their children. It simply helps to ensure health care for all. As Colgrove pointed out in his essay on ethics and politics associated with an HPV vaccine,

> Minors have a right to be protected against vaccine-preventable illness, and society has an interest in safeguarding the welfare of children who may be harmed by the choices of their parents and guardians.[16]

Justice

The risks of polio, STIs, and cancer are present in society, and all people, regardless of age, are exposed to these health problems, albeit at different rates during different stages of life. It would be wrong, according to Rawls's principle of justice, to provide health care to one group and withhold health care from another group because of a bias about age, race, gender, socioeconomic status, religion, or other factors.[12] The opportunity for justice, according to Rawls, should be provided to all impartially. This principle implies that an HPV vaccine should be made available to everyone in need. Universal access is fair, and withholding the vaccine on grounds of age, potential sexual behavior, or competing values about sexual engagement among youths is unfair. . . .

A compulsory vaccination program will better serve populations that are at greatest risk and in most need of health care and social justice. A utilitarian cost–benefit approach may lead to the greatest good for the greatest number of people, but a compulsory approach may produce the greatest utility for populations who are at greatest risk of disease. A compulsory vaccination program, therefore, appears to be a better alternative for ensuring justice and a fair opportunity for all in reducing harm caused by HPV infections.

Scientific Concerns About Compulsory Vaccination

Concerns have been raised in the scientific literature about mandating an HPV vaccination. In general, these objections evolve from a traditional utilitarian public health perspective that assesses the costs, benefits, outcomes, and risks of a compulsory vaccination program aimed at preventing health problems associated with HPV infection, including cervical cancer, that have low morbidity and mortality rates.

Scientists who question the use of a compulsory program recognize that an HPV vaccination can provide a highly effective means of protection from cervical cancer but caution against mandatory measures before research provides evidence of the vaccine's relative value. For example, Gostin and DeAngelis argue that the benefits from reducing an already low incidence rate of cervical cancer may be minimal.[13] Others assert that no imminent harm exists,[13–15] an alternative method of screening has been effective in reducing this threat,[13,14] achieving universal uptake will be difficult,[14] the vaccine is expensive,[13–15] long-term efficacy is not known,[31,32] and the ethics of limiting autonomy remains an issue.[13–16] . . .

In the United States, it is common to use vaccinations to reduce disease, including mandatory vaccinations for diseases such as measles and polio that have relatively low incidence rates for serious harm. The difference with HPV infection is that vaccination is being recommended to prevent cancer and genital warts that are related to sexual behavior, which raises moral, social, and scientific concerns among some segments of society. But youths who face the threat of STIs and cancer are in as great a need of disease prevention as children who faced the threat of polio in the 1950s. To withhold available and effective measures that prevent disease and death is immoral, as is advocating for alternative programs such as abstinence education that are unrealistic and ineffective.

Opposition in the scientific literature to compulsory vaccination arises from important and valid objections to an unspecified definition of imminent harm, given low rates of morbidity and mortality from cervical cancer and lack of long-term evidence for the safety and efficacy of the vaccine. However, there is precedent for mandating vaccinations against diseases that have low incidence rates of serious harm. Although the vaccine is less effective for sexually active women, it is nonetheless an important preventive measure for young women who have not been exposed to HPV types 16 and 18.

The HPV vaccine is not a replacement for cervical cancer screening and treatment. Rather, as Saraiya suggested, it is an additional and valuable tool for fighting cancer.[17] Combining a 70% reduction of cervical cancer by vaccination with the 80% efficacy of screening and treatment of cervical cancer will achieve a greater good for society than can be produced by either of these health measures alone. In addition, although vaccination will not eliminate the continued need to improve screening methods for detecting cervical cancer, it could potentially reduce the need for the intrusive treatment required for cervical cancer.

As more becomes known about the long-term consequences of an HPV vaccine, it is reasonable to hope that the goals of science—development of a safe and effective vaccine—will ally with moral ideals to offer all citizens equal access to a vaccine that reduces harm, which will be especially valuable to the disadvantaged populations at greatest risk. Ideally, this would occur on a voluntary basis, but history teaches us that it will be best accomplished by implementation of a compulsory vaccination program.

Some have proposed as an ethical test for mandatory public health polices that such policies can only be justified if voluntary measures have failed, no less coercive alternatives exist, the scientific rationale is compelling, and members of the general public are unknowingly at risk. I propose that the rightness or wrongness of a compulsory vaccination program should be determined from a public health perspective by assessing whether key ethical principles justify such action, whether the action reduces harm to individuals and society, and whether the action produces consequences that are at least as good as, if not better than, alternative actions that are present in society for preventing disease and death. Compulsory HPV vaccination meets this test.

Human Participant Protection

No protocol approval was required because no human participants were involved.

References

1. Smith JS. *Patenting the Sun: Polio and the Salk Vaccine.* New York, NY: William Morrow; 1990.

2. Centers for Disease Control and Prevention. *Epidemiology and Prevention of Vaccine-Preventable Diseases: The Pink Book.* 9th ed. Washington, DC: Public Health Foundation; 2006. Available at: http://www.cdc.gov/vaccine/pubs/pinkbook/pink-test.htm. Accessed June 15, 2007.

3. Cono J, Alexander LN. Poliomyelitis. In: Roush SW, McIntyre L, Baldy LM, eds. *VPD Surveillance Manual.* 3rd ed. Atlanta, GA: Centers for Disease Control and Prevention; 2002. http://www.cdc.gov/vaccines/pubs/sur-manual/downloads/chpt10_polio.pdf. Accessed November 20, 2007.

4. Meldrum M. "A calculated risk": The Salk polio vaccine field trials of 1954. *BMJ.* 1998;317(31):1233–1236.

5. Centers for Disease Control and Prevention. Ten great public health achievements—United States, 1900–1999. *MMWR Morb Mortal Wkly Rep.* 1999;48:241–243. http://www.cdc.gov/mmwr/preview/mmwrhtlm/00056796.htm. Accessed April 10, 1999.

6. Mill JS. *On Liberty.* New York, NY: Bobbs-Merrill; 1956.

7. Blake SM, Ledsky R, Goodenow C, Sawyer R, Lohrmann D, Windsor R. Condom availability programs in Massachusetts high schools: relationships with condom use and sexual behavior. *Am J Public Health.* 2003;93:955–962.

8. Centers for Disease Control and Prevention. National and state-specific pregnancy rates among adolescents—United States, 1995–1997. *MMWR Morb Mortal Wkly Rep.* 2000;49:605–611.

YES / Joseph E. Balog   **207**

9. Eaton DK, Kann L, Kinchen S, et al. Youth risk behavior surveillance—United States, 2005. *J Sch Health.* 2006;76:353–372.

10. Finer LB. Trends in premarital sex in the United States, 1954–2003. *Public Health Rep.* 2007;122(1):73–78.

11. Kann L, Kinchen SA, Williams BI, Ross JG, Lowry R, Grunbaum JA, Kolbe LJ. Youth risk behavior surveillance United States, 1999. *MMWR Morb Mortal Surveill Summ.* 2000;49(SS-5):1–96. http://www.cdc.gov/mmwr/preview/mmwrhtml/ss4905a1.htm. Accessed December 31, 2008.

12. Rawls J. *Theory of Justice.* Cambridge, MA: Harvard University Press; 1971.

13. Gostin LO, DeAngelis CD. Mandatory HPV vaccination: public health vs private wealth. *JAMA.* 2007;297(17):1921–1923.

14. Raffle AE. Challenges of implementing human papillomavirus (HPV) vaccination policy. *BMJ.* 2007;335(7616):375–377.

15. Udesky L. Push to mandate HPV vaccine triggers backlash in USA. *Lancet.* 2007;369:979–980.

16. Colgrove J. The ethics and politics of compulsory HPV vaccination. *N Engl J Med.* 2006;355(23):2389–2391.

17. Saraiya M, Ahmed F, Krishnan S, Richards TB, Unger ER, Lawson HW. Cervical cancer incidence in a prevaccine era in the United States, 1998–2002. *Obstet Gynecol.* 2007;109(2 pt 1):60–70.

Gail Javitt, Deena Berkowitz, and Lawrence O. Gostin

Assessing Mandatory HPV Vaccination: Who Should Call the Shots?

Why Mandating HPV Is Premature

The approval of a vaccine against cancer-causing HPV strains is a significant public health advance. Particularly in developing countries, which lack the health care resources for routine cervical cancer screening, preventing HPV infection has the potential to save millions of lives. In the face of such a dramatic advance, opposing government-mandated HPV vaccination may seem foolhardy, if not heretical. Yet strong legal, ethical, and policy arguments underlie our position that state-mandated HPV vaccination of minor females is premature.

A. Long-Term Safety and Effectiveness of the Vaccine Is Unknown

Although the aim of clinical trials is to generate safety and effectiveness data that can be extrapolated to the general population, it is widely understood that such trials cannot reveal all possible adverse events related to a product. For this reason, post-market adverse event reporting is required for all manufacturers of FDA-approved products, and post-market surveillance (also called "phase IV studies") may be required in certain circumstances. There have been numerous examples in recent years in which unforeseen adverse reactions following product approval led manufacturers to withdraw their product from the market. . . .

In the case of HPV vaccine, short-term clinical trials in thousands of young women did not reveal serious adverse effects. However, the adverse events reported since the vaccine's approval are, at the very least, a sobering reminder that rare adverse events may surface as the vaccine is administered to millions of girls and young women. Concerns have also been raised that other carcinogenic HPV types not contained in the vaccines will replace HPV types 16 and 18 in the pathological niche.

The duration of HPV vaccine-induced immunity is unclear. The average follow-up period for Gardasil during clinical trials was 15 months after the third dose of the vaccine. Determining long-term efficacy is complicated by the fact that even during naturally occurring HPV infection, HPV antibodies are not detected in many women. Thus, long-term, follow-up post-licensure studies cannot rely solely upon serologic measurement of HPV-induced antibody titers. . . .

The current ACIP recommendation is based on assumptions about duration of immunity and age of sexual debut, among other factors. As the vaccine is used for a longer time period, it may turn out that a different vaccine schedule is more effective. In addition, the effect on co-administration of other vaccines with regard to safety is unknown, as is the vaccines' efficacy with varying dose intervals. Some have also raised concerns about a negative impact of vaccination on cervical cancer screening programs, which are highly effective at reducing cervical cancer mortality. These unknowns must be studied as the vaccine is introduced in the broader population.

At present, therefore, questions remain about the vaccine's safety and the duration of its immunity, which call into question the wisdom of mandated vaccination. Girls receiving the vaccine face some risk of potential adverse events as well as risk that the vaccine will not be completely protective. These risks must be weighed against the state's interest in protecting the public from the harms associated with HPV. As discussed in the next section, the state's interest in protecting the public health does not support mandating HPV vaccination.

B. Historical Justifications for Mandated Vaccination Are Not Met

HPV is different in several respects from the vaccines that first led to state-mandated vaccination. Compulsory vaccination laws originated in the early 1800s and were driven by fears of the centuries-old scourge of smallpox and the advent of the vaccine developed by Edward Jenner in 1796. By the 1900s, the vast majority of states had enacted compulsory smallpox vaccination laws.[1] While such laws were not initially tied to school attendance, the coincidental rise of smallpox outbreaks, growth in the number of public schools, and compulsory school attendance laws provided a rationale for compulsory vaccination to prevent the spread of smallpox among school children as well as a means to enforce the requirement by barring unvaccinated children from school.[2] In 1827, Boston became the first city to require all children entering public school to provide evidence of vaccination.[3] Similar laws were enacted by several states during the latter half of the 19th century.[4]

The theory of herd immunity, in which the protective effect of vaccines extends beyond the vaccinated individual to others in the population, is the driving force behind mass immunization programs. Herd immunity theory proposes that, in diseases passed from person to person, it is difficult to maintain a chain of infection when large numbers of a population are immune. With the increase in number of immune individuals present in a population, the lower the likelihood that a susceptible person will come into contact with an infected individual. There is no threshold value above which herd immunity exists, but as vaccination rates increase, indirect protection also increases until the infection is eliminated. . . .

The smallpox laws of the 19th century, which were almost without exception upheld by the courts, helped lay the foundation for modern immunization statutes. Many modern-era laws were enacted in response to the transmission of measles in schools in the 1960s and 1970s. In 1977, the federal government launched the Childhood Immunization Initiative, which stressed the importance of strict enforcement of school immunization laws.[5] Currently, all states mandate vaccination as a condition for school entry, and in deciding whether to mandate vaccines, are guided by ACIP recommendations. At present, ACIP recommends vaccination for diphtheria, tetanus, and acellular pertussis (DTaP), Hepatitis B, polio, measles, mumps, and rubella (MMR), varicella (chicken pox), influenza, rotavirus, haemophilus Influenza B (HiB), pneumococcus, Hepatitis A, meningococcus, and, most recently HPV. State mandates differ; for example, whereas all states require DTaP, polio, and measles in order to enter kindergarten, most do not require Hepatitis A.[6]

HPV is different from the vaccines that have previously been mandated by the states. With the exception of tetanus, all of these vaccines fit comfortably within the "public health necessity" principle articulated in *Jacobson* [v. *Massachusetts* (1905)], in that the diseases they prevent are highly contagious and are associated with significant morbidity and mortality occurring shortly after exposure. And, while tetanus is not contagious, exposure to *Clostridium tetani* is both virtually unavoidable (particularly by children, given their propensity to both play in the dirt and get scratches), life threatening, and fully preventable only through vaccination. Thus, the public health necessity argument plausibly extends to tetanus, albeit for different reasons.

Jacobson's "reasonable relationship" principle is also clearly met by vaccine mandates for the other ACIP recommended vaccines. School-aged children are most at risk while in school because they are more likely to be in close proximity to each other in that setting. All children who attend school are equally at risk of both transmitting and contracting the diseases. Thus, a clear relationship exists between conditioning school attendance on vaccination and the avoidance of the spread of infectious disease within the school environment. Tetanus, a non-contagious disease, is somewhat different, but school-based vaccination can nevertheless be justified in that children will foreseeably be exposed within the school environment (e.g., on the playground) and, if exposed, face a high risk of mortality.

HPV vaccination, in contrast, does not satisfy these two principles. HPV infection presents no public health necessity, as that term was used in the context of *Jacobson*. While non-sexual transmission routes are theoretically possible, they have not been demonstrated. Like other sexually transmitted diseases which primarily affect adults, it is not immediately life threatening; as such, cervical cancer, if developed, will not manifest for years if not decades. Many women will never be exposed to the cancer-causing strains of HPV; indeed the prevalence of these strains in the U.S. is quite low. Furthermore, many who are exposed will not go on to develop cervical cancer. Thus, conditioning school attendance on HPV vaccination serves only to coerce compliance in the absence of a public health emergency.[7]

NO / Gail Javitt et al.   **211**

The relationship between the government's objective of preventing cervical cancer in women and the means used to achieve it—that is, vaccination of all girls as a condition of school attendance—lacks sufficient rationality. First, given that HPV is transmitted through sexual activity, exposure to HPV is not directly related to school attendance.[8] Second, not all children who attend school are at equal risk of exposure to or transmission of the virus. Those who abstain from sexual conduct are not at risk for transmitting or contracting HPV. Moreover, because HPV screening tests are available, the risk to those who choose to engage in sexual activity is significantly minimized. Because it is questionable how many school-aged children are actually at risk—and for those who are at risk, the risk is not linked to school attendance—there is not a sufficiently rational reason to tie mandatory vaccination to school attendance.

To be sure, the public health objective that proponents of mandatory HPV vaccination seek to achieve is compelling. Vaccinating girls before sexual debut provides an opportunity to provide protection against an adult onset disease. This opportunity is lost once sexual activity begins and exposure to HPV occurs. However, that HPV vaccination may be both medically justified and a prudent public health measure is an insufficient basis for the state to compel children to receive the vaccine as a condition of school attendance.

C. In the Absence of Historical Justification, the Government Risks Public Backlash by Mandating HPV Vaccination

Childhood vaccination rates in the United States are very high; more than half of the states report meeting the Department of Health and Human Services (HHS) Healthy People 2010 initiative's goal of ≥95 percent vaccination coverage for childhood vaccination.[9] However, from its inception, state mandated vaccination has been accompanied by a small but vocal anti-vaccination movement. Opposition has historically been "fueled by general distrust of government, a rugged sense of individualism, and concerns about the efficacy and safety of vaccines."[10] In recent years, vaccination programs also have been a "victim of their tremendous success,"[11] as dreaded diseases such as measles and polio have largely disappeared in the United States, taking with them the fear that motivated past generations. Some have noted with alarm the rise in the number of parents opting out of vaccination and of resurgence in anti-vaccination rhetoric making scientifically unsupported allegations that vaccination causes adverse events such as autism.[12]

The rash of state legislation to mandate HPV has led to significant public concern that the government is overreaching its police powers authority. As one conservative columnist has written, "[F]or the government to mandate the expensive vaccine for children would be for Big Brother to reach past the parents and into the home."[13] While some dismiss sentiments such as this one as simply motivated by right wing moral politics, trivializing these concerns is both inappropriate and unwise as a policy matter. Because sexual behavior is involved in transmission, not all children are equally at risk. Thus, it is a reasonable exercise of a parent's judgment to consider his or her child's specific risk and weigh that against the risk of vaccination.

To remove parental autonomy in this case is not warranted and also risks parental rejection of the vaccine because it is perceived as coercive. In contrast, educating the public about the value of the vaccine may be highly effective without risking public backlash. According to one poll, 61 percent of parents with daughters under 18 prefer vaccination, 72 percent would support the inclusion of information about the vaccine in school health classes, and just 45 percent agreed that the vaccine should be included as part of the vaccination routine for all children and adolescents.[14]

Additionally, Merck's aggressive role in lobbying for the passage of state laws mandating HPV has led to some skepticism about whether profit rather than public health has driven the push for state mandates.[15] Even one proponent of state-mandated HPV vaccination acknowledges that Merck "overplayed its hand" by pushing hard for legislation mandating the vaccine.[16] In the face of such criticisms, the company thus ceased its lobbying efforts but indicated it would continue to educate health officials and legislators about the vaccine.[17]

Some argue that liberal opt-out provisions will take care of the coercion and distrust issues. Whether this is true will depend in part on the reasons for which a parent may opt out and the ease of opting out. For example, a parent may not have a religious objection to vaccination in general, but nevertheless may not feel her 11-year-old daughter is at sufficient risk for HPV to warrant vaccination. This sentiment may or may not be captured in a "religious or philosophical" opt-out provision.

Even if opt-out provisions do reduce public distrust issues for HPV, however, liberal opt outs for one vaccine may have a negative impact on other vaccine programs. Currently, with the exception of those who opt out of all vaccines on religious or philosophical grounds, parents must accept all mandated vaccines because no vaccine-by-vaccine selection process exists, which leads to a high rate of vaccine coverage. Switching to an "a la carte" approach, in which parents can consider the risks and benefits of vaccines on a vaccine-by-vaccine basis, would set a dangerous precedent and may lead them to opt out of other vaccines, causing a rise in the transmission of these diseases. In contrast, an "opt in" approach to HPV vaccine would not require a change in the existing paradigm and would still likely lead to a high coverage rate.

Conclusion

Based on the current scientific evidence, vaccinating girls against HPV before they are sexually active appears to provide significant protection against cervical cancer. The vaccine thus represents a significant public health advance. Nevertheless, mandating HPV vaccination at the present time would be premature and ill-advised. The vaccine is relatively new, and long-term safety and effectiveness in the general population is unknown. Vaccination outcomes of those voluntarily vaccinated should be followed for several years before mandates are imposed. Additionally, the HPV vaccine does not represent a public health necessity of the type that has justified previous vaccine mandates. State mandates could therefore lead to a public backlash that will undermine

NO / Gail Javitt et al.   **213**

both HPV vaccination efforts and existing vaccination programs. Finally, the economic consequences of mandating HPV are significant and could have a negative impact on financial support for other vaccines as well as other public health programs. These consequences should be considered before HPV is mandated.

The success of childhood vaccination programs makes them a tempting target for the addition of new vaccines that, while beneficial to public health, exceed the original justifications for the development of such programs and impose new financial burdens on both the government, private physicians, and, ultimately, the public. HPV will not be the last disease that state legislatures will attempt to prevent through mandatory vaccination. Thus, legislatures and public health advocates should consider carefully the consequences of altering the current paradigm for mandatory childhood vaccination and should not mandate HPV vaccination in the absence of a new paradigm to justify such an expansion.

Note

The views expressed in this article are those of the author and do not reflect those of the Genetics and Public Policy Center or its staff.

References

1. J. G. Hodge and L. O. Gostin, "School Vaccination Requirements: Historical, Social, and Legal Perspectives," *Kentucky Law Journal* 90, no. 4 (2001–2002): 831–890.

2. J. Duffy, "School Vaccination: The Precursor to School Medical Inspection," *Journal of the History of Medicine and Allied Sciences* 33, no. 3 (1978): 344–355.

3. See Hodge and Gostin, *supra* note 1.

4. *Id.*

5. A. R. Hinman et al., "Childhood Immunization: Laws that Work," *Journal of Law, Medicine & Ethics* 30, no. 3 (2002): 122–127; K. M. Malone and A. R. Hinman, "Vaccination Mandates: The Public Health Imperative and Individual Rights," in R. A. Goodman et al., *Law in Public Health Practice* (New York: Oxford University Press, 2006).

6. Centers for Disease Control and Prevention, *Childcare and School Immunization Requirements, 2005–2006,* August 2006, *available at* <http://www.immunize.org/laws/2005-06_izrequirements.pdf> (last visited March 5, 2008).

7. B. Lo, "HPV Vaccine and Adolescents' Sexual Activity: It Would Be a Shame If Unresolved Ethical Dilemmas Hampered This Breakthrough," *BMJ* 332, no. 7550 (2006): 1106–1107.

8. R. K. Zimmerman, "Ethical Analysis of HPV Vaccine Policy Options," *Vaccine* 24, no. 22 (2006): 4812–4820.

9. C. Stanwyck et al., "Vaccination Coverage Among Children Entering School—United States, 2005–06 School Year," *JAMA* 296, no. 21 (2006): 2544–2547.

214   ISSUE 11 / Should Vaccination for HPV Be Mandated for Teenage . . . ?

10. See Hodge and Gostin, *supra* note 1.

11. S. P. Calandrillo, "Vanishing Vaccinations: Why Are So Many Americans Opting Out of Vaccinating Their Children?" *University of Michigan Journal of Legal Reform* 37 (2004): 353–440.

12. *Id.*

13. B. Hart, "My Daughter Won't Get HPV Vaccine," *Chicago Sun Times,* February 25, 2007, at B6.

14. J. Cummings, "Seventy Percent of U.S. Adults Support Use of the Human Papillomavirus (HPV) Vaccine: Majority of Parents of Girls under 18 Would Want Daughters to Receive It," *Wall Street Journal Online* 5, no. 13 (2006). . . .

15. J. Marbella, "Sense of Rush Infects Plan to Require HPV Shots," *Baltimore Sun*, January 30, 2007. . . .

16. S. Reimer, "Readers Worry About HPV Vaccine: Doctors Say It's Safe," *Baltimore Sun*, April 3, 2007.

17. A. Pollack and S. Saul, "Lobbying for Vaccine to Be Halted," *New York Times,* February 21, 2007. . . .

POSTSCRIPT

Should Vaccination for HPV Be Mandated for Teenage Girls?

In October 2008, the CDC announced that one in four girls aged 13–17 have been vaccinated with Gardasil since its introduction. This is a lower percentage that vaccine advocates had anticipated.

According to the National Conference of State Legislatures, in 2007 at least 24 states and the District of Columbia introduced legislation specifically mandating a school HPV vaccine requirement. Of these, only the District of Columbia's bill was enacted, with enforcement to start 30 days after the Congressional Review Period expired. Other state legislatures are moving more slowly; although most legislatures have considered the issue, when they have acted, they have mostly provided funds for voluntary vaccination or for educational programs for the public. For a complete list of state legislation, go to http://www.ncsl.org/programs/health/HPVVaccine.htm.

On August 1, 2008, the HPV vaccine became one of the required vaccinations for young immigrant females. A 1996 immigration law requires applicants for a green card (legal entry into the United States) have all the vaccinations recommended (not required) by the CDC. This action has been criticized by many immigration advocates and even members of the original CDC panel that recommended the use of the vaccine, as well as Merck representatives. Even though only one dose is required, this adds about $120 to an already expensive list of requirements (*Wall Street Journal*, October 1, 2008).

Although the European Union has approved the use of another HPV vaccine, GlaxoSmithKline's Cervarix, the FDA has not done so yet.

J. L. Schwartz, A. L. Caplan, R. R. Faden, and J. Sugarman review the "unexpectedly early" activity in state legislatures from an ethical perspective ("Lessons from the Failure of Human Papillomavirus Vaccine State Requirments," *Clinical Pharmacological Therapy*, December 2007). R. I. Field and A. L. Caplan see the controversy as one between autonomy (in this case freedom from government intrusion) and beneficence, utilitarianism, and justice, all of which lend support to intervention. They would support a mandate based on utilitarianism if certain conditions are met and if "herd immunity" (protecting the community by vaccinating the few) is a realistic objective ("A Proposed Ethical Framework for Vaccine Mandates: Competing Values and the Case of HPV," *Kennedy Institute of Ethical Journal*, June 2008).

For additional commentary on the HPV vaccine, see these articles in the May 10, 2007, issue of *The New England Journal of Medicine*: George F. Sawaya and Karen Smith-McCune, "HPV Vaccination—More Answers, More Questions"; Lindsey R. Baden, Gregory D. Curfman, Stephen Morrissey, and

Jeffry M. Drazen, "Human Papillomavirus Vaccine—Opportunity and Challenge"; Jan M. Agosti and Sue J. Goldie, "Introducing HPV Vaccine in Developing Countries—Key Challenges and Issues." The scientific report that inspired these commentaries, also in this issue, is "Quadrivalent Vaccine against Human Papillomavirus to Prevent High-Grade Cervical Lesions," by The FUTURE II Study Group.

Internet References . . .

Human Genome Project Information

This site contains information on the ethics, legal, and social issues related to advances in genetics.

http://www.ornl.gov/sci/techresources/Human_Genome/elsi.shtml

President's Council on Bioethics

This site has all the reports on cloning and stem cell research of this council, as well as those of prior commissions.

http://www.bioethics.gov

Council for Responsible Genetics

This organization has a newsletter and articles on the political, medical, consumer, and scientific aspects of genetics.

http://www.gene-watch.org

The Case Against Perfection

Breakthroughs in genetics present us with a promise and a predicament. The promise is that we may soon be able to treat and prevent a host of debilitating diseases. The predicament is that our newfound genetic knowledge may also enable us to manipulate our own nature—to enhance our muscles, memories, and moods; to choose the sex, height, and other genetic traits of our children; to make ourselves "better than well." When science moves faster than moral understanding, as it does today, men and women struggle to articulate their unease. In liberal societies they reach first for the language of autonomy, fairness, and individual rights. But this part of our moral vocabulary is ill equipped to address the hardest questions posed by genetic engineering. The genomic revolution has induced a kind of moral vertigo. . . .

In order to grapple with the ethics of enhancement, we need to confront questions largely lost from view—questions about the moral status of nature, and about the proper stance of human beings toward the given world. Since these questions verge on theology, modern philosophers and political theorists tend to shrink from them. But our new powers of biotechnology make them unavoidable. To see why this is so, consider four examples already on the horizon: muscle enhancement, memory enhancement, growth-hormone treatment, and reproductive technologies that enable parents to choose the sex and some genetic traits of their children. In each case what began as an attempt to treat a disease or prevent a genetic disorder now beckons as an instrument of improvement and consumer choice.

Muscles   Everyone would welcome a gene therapy to alleviate muscular dystrophy and to reverse the debilitating muscle loss that comes with old age. But what if the same therapy were used to improve athletic performance? Researchers have developed a synthetic gene that, when injected into the muscle cells of mice, prevents and even reverses natural muscle deterioration. The gene not only repairs wasted or injured muscles but also strengthens healthy ones. This success bodes well for human applications. H. Lee Sweeney, of the University of Pennsylvania, who leads the research, hopes his discovery will cure the immobility that afflicts the elderly. But Sweeney's bulked-up mice have already attracted the attention of athletes seeking a competitive edge. Although the therapy is not yet approved for human use, the prospect of genetically enhanced weight lifters, home-run sluggers, linebackers, and sprinters is easy to imagine. The widespread use of steroids and other performance-improving problem. By 1996 such "off-label" use accounted for 40 percent of human-growth-hormone prescriptions. Although it is legal to prescribe drugs for purposes not approved by the Food and Drug Administration, pharmaceutical companies cannot promote such use. Seeking to expand its market, Eli Lilly & Co. recently persuaded the FDA to approve its human growth hormone for healthy children whose projected adult height is in the bottom one percentile—under five feet three inches for boys and four feet eleven inches for girls. This concession raises a large question about the ethics of enhancement: If hormone treatments need not be limited to those with hormone deficiencies, why should they be available only to very short children? Why shouldn't all shorter-than-average children be able to seek treatment? And what about a child of average height who wants to be taller so that he can make the basketball team?

Some oppose height enhancement on the grounds that it is collectively self-defeating; as some become taller, others become shorter relative to the norm. Except in Lake Wobegon, not every child can be above average. As the unenhanced began to feel shorter, they, too, might seek treatment, leading to a hormonal arms race that left everyone worse off, especially those who couldn't afford to buy their way up from shortness.

But the arms-race objection is not decisive on its own. Like the fairness objection to bioengineered muscles and memory, it leaves unexamined the attitudes and dispositions that prompt the drive for enhancement. If we were bothered only by the injustice of adding shortness to the problems of the poor, we could remedy that unfairness by publicly subsidizing height enhancements. As for the relative height deprivation suffered by innocent bystanders, we could compensate them by taxing those who buy their way to greater height. The real question is whether we want to live in a society where parents feel compelled to spend a fortune to make perfectly healthy kids a few inches taller.

Sex selection   Perhaps the most inevitable nonmedical use of bioengineering is sex selection. For centuries parents have been trying to choose the sex of their children. Today biotech succeeds where folk remedies failed.

One technique for sex selection arose with prenatal tests using amniocentesis and ultrasound. These medical technologies were developed to detect genetic abnormalities such as spina bifida and Down syndrome. But they can also reveal the sex of the fetus—allowing for the abortion of a fetus of an undesired sex. Even among those who favor abortion rights, few advocate abortion simply because the parents do not want a girl. Nevertheless, in traditional societies with a powerful cultural preference for boys, this practice has become widespread. . . .

It is commonly said that genetic enhancements undermine our humanity by threatening our capacity to act freely, to succeed by our own efforts, and to consider ourselves responsible—worthy of praise or blame—for the things we do and for the way we are. . . .

Though there is much to be said for this argument, I do not think the main problem with enhancement and genetic engineering is that they undermine effort and erode human agency. The deeper danger is that they represent a kind of hyperagency—a Promethean aspiration to remake nature, including human nature, to serve our purposes and satisfy our desires. The problem is not the drift to mechanism but the drive to mastery. And what the drive to mastery misses and may even destroy is an appreciation of the gifted character of human powers and achievements.

To acknowledge the giftedness of life is to recognize that our talents and powers are not wholly our own doing, despite the effort we expend to develop and to exercise them. It is also to recognize that not everything in the world is open to whatever use we may desire or devise. Appreciating the gifted quality of life constrains the Promethean project and conduces to a certain humility. It is in part a religious sensibility. But its resonance reaches beyond religion. . . .

The ethic of giftedness, under siege in sports, persists in the practice of parenting. But here, too, bioengineering and genetic enhancement threaten to dislodge it. To appreciate children as gifts is to accept them as they come, not as objects of our design or products of our will or instruments of our ambition. Parental love is not contingent on the talents and attributes a child happens to have. We choose our friends and spouses at least partly on the basis of qualities we find attractive. But we do not choose our children. Their qualities are unpredictable, and even the most conscientious parents cannot be held wholly responsible for the kind of children they have. That is why parenthood, more than other human relationships, teaches what the theologian William F. May calls an "openness to the unbidden."

May's resonant phrase helps us see that the deepest moral objection to enhancement lies less in the perfection it seeks than in the human disposition it expresses and promotes. The problem is not that parents usurp the autonomy of a child they design. The problem lies in the hubris of the designing parents, in their drive to master the mystery of birth. Even if this disposition did not make parents tyrants to their children, it would disfigure the relation between parent and child, and deprive the parent of the humility and enlarged human sympathies that an openness to the unbidden can cultivate.

To appreciate children as gifts or blessings is not, of course, to be passive in the face of illness or disease. Medical intervention to cure or prevent illness or restore the injured to health does not desecrate nature but honors it. Healing sickness or injury does not override a child's natural capacities but permits them to flourish.

Nor does the sense of life as a gift mean that parents must shrink from shaping and directing the development of their child. Just as athletes and artists have an obligation to cultivate their talents, so parents have an obligation to cultivate their children, to help them discover and develop their talents and gifts. As May points out, parents give their children two kinds of love: accepting love and transforming love. Accepting love affirms the being of the child, whereas transforming love seeks the well-being of the child. Each aspect corrects the excesses of the other, he writes: "Attachment becomes too quietistic if it slackens into mere acceptance of the child as he is." Parents have a duty to promote their children's excellence.

These days, however, overly ambitious parents are prone to get carried away with transforming love—promoting and demanding all manner of accomplishments from their children, seeking perfection. "Parents find it difficult to maintain an equilibrium between the two sides of love," May observes. "Accepting love, without transforming love, slides into indulgence and finally neglect. Transforming love, without accepting love, badgers and finally rejects." May finds in these competing impulses a parallel with modern science: it, too, engages us in beholding the given world, studying and savoring it, and also in molding the world, transforming and perfecting it.

The mandate to mold our children, to cultivate and improve them, complicates the case against enhancement. We usually admire parents who seek the best for their children, who spare no effort to help them achieve happiness and success. Some parents confer advantages on their children by enrolling them in expensive schools, hiring private tutors, sending them to tennis camp, providing them with piano lessons, ballet lessons, swimming lessons, SAT-prep courses, and so on. If it is permissible and even admirable for parents to help their children in these ways, why isn't it equally admirable for parents to use whatever genetic technologies may emerge (provided they are safe) to enhance their children's intelligence, musical ability, or athletic prowess?

The defenders of enhancement are right to this extent: improving children through genetic engineering is similar in spirit to the heavily managed, high-pressure child-rearing that is now common. But this similarity does not vindicate genetic enhancement. On the contrary, it highlights a problem with the trend toward hyperparenting. One conspicuous example of this trend is sports-crazed parents bent on making champions of their children. Another is the frenzied drive of overbearing parents to mold and manage their children's academic careers. . . .

Some see a clear line between genetic enhancement and other ways that people seek improvement in their children and themselves. Genetic manipulation seems somehow worse—more intrusive, more sinister—than other ways of enhancing performance and seeking success. But morally speaking, the difference is less significant than it seems. Bioengineering gives us reason to question the low-tech, high-pressure child-rearing practices we commonly accept. The hyperparenting familiar in our time represents an anxious excess of mastery and dominion that misses the sense of life as a gift. . . .

In a social world that prizes mastery and control, parenthood is a school for humility. That we care deeply about our children and yet cannot choose the kind we want teaches parents to be open to the unbidden. Such openness is a disposition worth affirming, not only within families but in the wider world as well. It invites us to abide the unexpected, to live with dissonance, to rein in the impulse to control. A *Gattaca*-like world in which parents became accustomed to specifying the sex and genetic traits of their children would be a world inhospitable to the unbidden, a gated community writ large. The awareness that our talents and abilities are not wholly our own doing restrains our tendency toward hubris. . . .

There is something appealing, even intoxicating, about a vision of human freedom unfettered by the given. It may even be the case that the

YES / Michael J. Sandel   **227**

allure of that vision played a part in summoning the genomic age into being. It is often assumed that the powers of enhancement we now possess arose as an inadvertent by-product of biomedical progress—the genetic revolution came, so to speak, to cure disease, and stayed to tempt us with the prospect of enhancing our performance, designing our children, and perfecting our nature. That may have the story backwards. It is more plausible to view genetic engineering as the ultimate expression of our resolve to see ourselves astride the world, the masters of our nature. But that promise of mastery is flawed. It threatens to banish our appreciation of life as a gift, and to leave us with nothing to affirm or behold outside our own will.

Howard Trachtman

A Man Is a Man Is a Man

Every field of human endeavor goes through a period of great anticipation in which the leading lights predict that the end of the discipline is near and that acquisition of new knowledge in the area is almost complete. Thus, at the end of the nineteenth century, physicists were confident that they had natural order of things under control and that mastery of the physical world was just a matter of time. A few decades later, David Hilbert and colleagues asserted that they were closing in on verification of the internal consistency and validity of mathematics and by inference all of philosophy (Goldstein 2005). In the early 1970s, as immunization practice and administration of antibiotics became standard and scourges of earlier eras like smallpox and polio were vanishing, specialists in infectious disease were sure that their field had things well in hand. Finally, after the fall of the Berlin Wall, Francis Fukuyama (1992) wrote confidently that history was at an end and that the global community was entering a phase of prosperity and harmony.

From the privileged vantage point of the early 21st century, we know how grandiose these predictions were. Einstein and his relativistic quanta, Godel and his incompleteness theorem, AIDS and Ebola, and the attack on the World Trade Center demonstrate that nothing ever goes quite exactly according to plan and that human beings still have plenty of work cut out for them.

In light of all of this sobering experience, it is surprising that physicians and bioethicists should have such unrealistic views and apprehensions about prospective therapeutic interventions that may arise from the remarkable advances in genetics or neurobiology. Michael Sandel's (2004) article is representative of this literature and Kamm's (2005) review is an insightful analysis of this position. However, I think it falls short on several practical points that should disarm anxious critics of enhancement.

Enhancement is a new term that is in vogue to describe what doctors have been doing since time immemorial, namely working to improve the lot of the patients they care for. Each medical advance from X-rays to imatinib has always been heralded as the advent of the new millennium only to be replaced by new problems or unexpected complications of old problems (Kantarjian et al. 2002). But, despite rapid approval and grand hopes, no enhancement or treatment has ever turned out to be all it was cracked up to be. Outcomes in real patients hardly ever live up to the exaggerated claims of the advanced sales

From *The American Journal of Bioethics*, vol. 5, no. 3, May/June 2005, pp. 31–33. Copyright © 2005 by Routledge/Taylor & Francis Group. Reprinted by permission via Rightslink. www.informaworld.com

pitch. With each answer that emerges from a clinical trial, there are even more questions that are raised about optimal efficacy, the best target population, and the appropriate balance of benefits and risks. Longer life spans means more cancer and dementia, more antibiotics mean more virulent organisms, improvements in neonatal care mean more damaged low birth weight survivors. Programs for medical enhancement will never deliver on all great expectations, either good or bad. As such there appears to be no inherent reason to fear enhancement or limit its application.

If enhancement represents the intrinsic nature of man to reach out and control his own fate by manipulating his environment and to reverse any adverse effects of his surroundings, then it is inappropriate to use the term mastery in describing this defining human capacity. Instead of considering enhancement an activity with automatic winners and losers, I suggest that it would clarify the discussion if it was viewed as a hard wired human trait that we all engage in. Some do it better than others but all of us try to enhance our lot in life as best as we can. It is undoubtedly true that knowledge can and will be misdirected and even abused by those interested in self-aggrandizement. However, again this is not a unique feature of the remarkable advances in genomics or imaging technology. The fact that there are Harry Limes in the world does not take away from the benefits of antibiotics. The abuse of erythropoietin by athletes does not detract from the qualitative improvement in the lives of patients with end stage renal disease who are treated with this drug (Schumacher et al. 2001).

Moreover, intent has always been a difficult barometer to gauge the behavior of any professional. Most patients are only interested in getting better or improving their health. They rarely concern themselves with the motivation of the care provider, be it money, fame, fortune, or an altruistic desire to help others. Similarly, physicians rarely question why people want to get better as long as they follow instructions and balance the risks and benefits reasonably in their health care judgments. Even in judging religious behavior, which must comply with extralegal concerns and varying standards of dogma, intent is usually implicitly assumed to be appropriate or ignored provided the outcome is not destructive to the individual or community. One would be hard pressed to see any advantage for the patients if individual doctors or the health profession as a whole got into the business of judging patients' intention when they seek a medical treatment to cure disease or enhance health. If there are any lessons to be drawn from the endless discussions about active and passive euthanasia, it may be that no one is served by making this fine distinction in clinical practice (Kamisar 1969).

Finally, the distinction that is being made between treatment which is justified and permissible *versus* enhancement which smacks of hubris and should be constrained may prove to be irrelevant in real life situations where the boundaries are blurred by rapid advances in medical therapeutics and the definition of disease itself. When is failure to concentrate a sign of disease worthy of treatment and when does it indicate a lazy student who is not willing to work hard enough in school? Is erectile dysfunction an ailment like salmonella enteritis or a failure to perform? If I can confidently help the patient with their problem safely and effectively, I for one would just as soon avoid categorizing their complaint into an acceptable *versus* unacceptable category.

Finally, what is intriguing is that those who frown upon physicians who would dispense treatments that enhance patients rather than treat a disease is the assumption that there will be near unanimous acceptance of the treatment and a groundswell of people requesting the therapy. However, a survey of the history of public health interventions indicates that people, at least in this country, are reluctant to take the words of doctors on faith. Although each advance reported in the press is greeted by the public with great fanfare and anticipation, in reality many treatments are rejected by large segments of the population. Think of the people who refuse immunizations for their child, who place greater credence in alternative medications instead of chemotherapy (Frederickson 2004). There will always be people in search for the quick fix to treat obesity, prevent dementia, or win an Olympic medal. But, I think it is contrary to experience to think that everyone will line up for each new genetic treatment or enhancement. Doctors would do well to remind themselves of how varied their patients really are and that application of any therapeutic advance will still begin with a sensitive dialogue between doctor and patient.

In conclusion, I would encourage the medical community to embrace enhancement as a never ending quest for health that will make us healthier but never perfect. We should not fear progress in diagnostics or try to limit medical manipulations. This is because experience teaches us that they will never meet their goals and always leave us striving for more. I endorse Kamm's proposal to promote education about appropriate utilization of advances in genetics and medical science, insure equitable use of these resources, and maintain surveillance for unanticipated and undesirable consequences. However, as it says in Ethics of the Fathers, "The day is short, the work is hard, the employees are tired, the reward is great, and the boss is pressing" (Babylonian Talmud, Ch. 2, Mishna, 20). But, at the end of the day, we will still be human and knowing that should give us the confidence to proceed.

Acknowledgement

The author wishes to thank Rachel Frank, R.N. for her thoughtful comments about this essay.

References

Frederickson, D. D., T. C. Davis, C. L. Arnould, et al. 2004. Childhood immunization refusal: Provider and parent perceptions. *Family Medicine* 36:431–439.

Fukuyama, F. 1992. *The end of history and the last man.* New York: Free Press.

Goldstein, R. 2005. Incompleteness: The proof and paradox of Kort Godel. New York: W.W. Norton & Co.

Kamisar, Y. 1969. Euthanasia legislation: Some non-religious objections. In *Euthanasia and the right to death,* ed. A. B. Downing, Los Angeles, CA: Nash Publishing Company.

Kamm, F. M. 2005. Is there a problem with enhancement? *Am. J. Bioethics* 5–14.

NO / Howard Trachtman   **231**

Kantarjian H., C. Sawyers, A. Hochhaus, et al. 2002. Hematologic and cytogenetic responses to imatinib mesylate in chronic myelogenous leukemia. *New England Journal of Medicine* 346:645–652.

Sandel, M. 2004. The case against perfection. *The Atlantic Monthly* 293(3): 51–62.

Schumacher, Y. O., A. Schmid, and T. Lenz. 2001. Blood testing in sports: Hematological profile of a convicted athlete. *Clinical Journal of Sport Medicine* 11:115–117.

POSTSCRIPT

Is Genetic Enhancement an Unacceptable Use of Technology?

None of the genetic enhancements that arouse either fear or anticipation are possible with current technologies. Some say that they will never be possible since most of the desired or unwelcome characteristics are not controlled by a single gene and are also affected by many other background factors. Still, the future may bring still-undreamed-of possibilities.

The issue of *The American Journal of Bioethics* (vol. 5, no. 3, 2005), from which Howard Trachtman's essay is drawn, also contains several other articles on enhancement. The lead article by Frances M. Kamm, "Is There a Problem with Enhancement?" analyzes Sandel's article from a philosophical perspective.

For a fuller explanation of Sandel's views, see his book *The Case Against Perfection: Ethics in the Age of Genetic Engineering* (Belknap Press, 2007). Also see Jonathan Glover, *Choosing Children: Genes, Disability, and Design* (Oxford University Press, 2008) for a perspective incorporating the viewpoints of people with disabilities.

Julian Savulescu argues that we have a moral obligation to enhance human beings and that "to be human is to strive to be better" ("New Breeds of Humans: The Moral Obligation to Enhance," *Reproductive Medicine Online,* March 2005). In "Enhancements and Justice: Problems in Determining the Requirements of Justice in a Genetically Transformed Society," Ronald A. Lindsay asserts that concern about the "threat of a genetic aristocracy" appears misplaced, given the already existing disparities in society (*Kennedy Institute of Ethics Journal,* vol. 15, no. 1, 2005).

Wondergenes: Genetic Enhancement and the Future of Society by Maxwell J. Mehlman (Indiana University Press, 2003) is an accessible introduction to the social and personal implications of genetic engineering. See also Erik Parens, "Authenticity and Ambivalence: Toward Understanding the Enhancement Debate," *Hastings Center Report* (May–June 2005).

Genetic enhancement to improve performance in sports is often rumored but not yet a reality, according to Thomas H. Murray in "Gene Doping and Olympic Sport" (*Play True,* issue 1, 2005). He points to the dangers of untested technologies to alter genetic makeup. See Issue 20, "Should Performance-Enhancing Drugs Be Banned from Sports?"

On the Web: "Genetic Enhancement" from the National Human Genome Research Institute, http://www.genome.gov/10004767.

ISSUE 4

Are We Winning the War on Cancer?

YES: John R. Seffrin, from "Winning the War on Cancer: Public Health or Public Policy Challenge?" *Vital Speeches of the Day* (September 2006)

NO: Reynold Spector, from "The War on Cancer: A Progress Report for Skeptics," *Skeptical Inquirer* (January/February 2010)

ISSUE SUMMARY

YES: American Cancer Society president John R. Seffrin claims we are winning the war against cancer and that it is possible to eliminate the disease as a major public health problem.

NO: Physician and professor of medicine Reynold Spector argues that the gains made against cancer have been limited and that overall there has been very little progress in the war on cancer.

Cancer is a group of diseases characterized by uncontrolled cellular growth, invasion that intrudes on and destroys nearby tissues, and may metastasize or spread to other locations in the body via blood or lymph. The malignant characteristics of cancers differentiate them from benign growths or tumors, which do not invade or metastasize. Fortunately, most cancers can be treated with drugs or chemotherapy, surgery, and/or radiation. The outcome of the disease is based on the type of cancer, for example, lung or breast, and the extent of disease. Although cancer affects people of all ages, and a few types of cancer are actually more common in children, most cancer risks increase with age. Cancer rates are increasing as more people live longer and lifestyles change such as increased smoking occur in the developing world.

Most cancers have an environmental link, with 90–95 percent of cases attributed to environmental factors and 5–10 percent due to heredity. Typical environmental factors that contribute to cancer deaths include diet and obesity (30–35 percent), smoking and tobacco use (25–30 percent), infectious agents (15–20 percent), and ionizing and nonionizing radiation (up to 10 percent). The remaining may be caused by stress, lack of exercise, and some environmental pollutants. Cancer prevention is related to those active measures that decrease the incidence of the disease. Since the vast majority of cancer risk factors are environmental or lifestyle-related, cancer is largely a preventable disease. Individuals who avoid tobacco, maintain a healthy weight, eat a diet rich in fruits and vegetables, exercise, use alcohol in moderation, take measures to prevent the transmission of sexually transmitted diseases, and avoid exposure to air pollution are likely to significantly reduce their risks of the disease.

Cancer's reputation is a deadly one. In reality, about half of the patients receiving treatment for invasive cancer will not survive the disease or the treatment. The survival rate, however, can vary significantly by the type of cancer, ranging from basically all patients surviving to almost no patients surviving. Predicting either short-term or long-term survival is challenging and depends on a variety of factors. The most important factors are the type of cancer and the patient's age and overall health. Medically frail patients suffering simultaneously from other illnesses have lower survival rates than otherwise healthy patients. Despite strong social pressure to maintain an upbeat, optimistic attitude or act like a determined "fighter" to "win the battle," research has not shown that personality traits have a connection to survival.

In 1971, the then president Richard Nixon signed the National Cancer Act of 1971. The goal of the act was to find a cure for cancer by increased research to improve the understanding of cancer biology and the development of more effective treatments such as targeted drug therapies. The act is also viewed as the beginning of the war on cancer and the vow to end the disease for good. Despite significant progress in the treatment of certain forms of cancer, the disease in general remains a major cause of death 40 years after this effort began, leading to a perceived lack of progress and to new legislation aimed at augmenting the original National Cancer Act of 1971. New research directions, in part based on the results of the Human Genome Project, hold promise for a better understanding of the hereditary factors underlying cancer and the development of new diagnostics, treatments, preventive measures, and early detection ability.

In the following selections, American Cancer Society President John R. Seffrin claims we are winning the war against cancer and that it is possible to eliminate the disease as a major public health problem. Physician and professor of medicine Reynold Spector argues that the gains made against cancer have been limited and that overall there has been very little progress in the war on cancer.

YES ↵

John R. Seffrin

Winning the War on Cancer: Public Health or Public Policy Challenge?

Ladies and gentlemen—we are winning!

For the first time—we can today state that we are winning the war on cancer.

What is even more—we now know essentially what it will take to finish the job—that is eliminating cancer as a major public health problem—first here in the US and then worldwide. Indeed, the progress made in our understanding of the cancer problem is so great—so substantial—that we find ourselves in a very different place—and in a very different situation—than when the American Cancer Society was founded in 1913 or even when the National Cancer Act was passed in 1971.

Today, we know more about cancer than ever before. We understand many of its causes. We know how to prevent it, and, we increasingly know how to cure it, especially in its early stages. Despite this significant growth in the knowledge base, we have not succeeded in stemming the growing burden of cancer. The gap between what is and what could be in cancer control and cancer care is the single most important issue facing the cancer community in the world today.

So it is in this context that I would like to share with you these four facts of life or new realities which form the core of my message today.

1. For the first time, we know what it will take to win the war on cancer, based on evidence.
2. We can eliminate cancer as a major health problem in the US in this century, if we do the right things.
3. However, if we fail to intervene—if we fail to do the right things, cancer will become the leading cause of death in the US by 2018 and eventually, likely, the leading cause of death in the world.
4. So the conquest of the world's most feared disease is a question of choice, priority, resources, and resolve, not luck or a magic bullet or a single miracle cure.

While the hopeful side of cancer has never been more hopeful—and the prospects for saving and improving lives are truly extraordinary—we do have our work cut out for us.

From *Vital Speeches of the Day*, September 2006.

YES / John R. Seffrin   **65**

Science alone, public health alone, or public policy alone cannot get us to where we need to be to realize this very possible dream. It will take all three and a lot of commitment and collaboration to make it happen. And as I speak, the cancer burden is actually getting worse—not better—and cancer will kill more people in the world this year than HIV/AIDS, tuberculosis, and malaria combined.

Perhaps ironically, in the last 60 years, science has made remarkable progress toward unraveling the mystery of cancer. But so much of what we know about cancer is not being adequately translated into what we do about cancer.

As a result, if current trends persist, by 2020, the number of new cancer cases worldwide will grow to 15 million and the number of deaths will double to as many as 12 million. An estimated 70 percent of these deaths will occur in developing countries, which are least prepared to address their growing cancer burdens.

With recent advances in our understanding of cancer, these are people whose lives need not be lost. They continue to experience unnecessary suffering and death not because we don't know how to prevent it or detect it early or treat it, but because we refuse to ensure that all people in all nations—including our own—have equal access to lifesaving cancer advances.

That's why this July the American Cancer Society is doing something that hasn't been done before—bringing together two world conferences that have rarely been held in the same year, and never in the same country—the World Cancer Congress and the 13th World Conference on Tobacco OR Health.

These two conferences will bring together over 5,500 participants from more than 130 countries: oncologists, public health leaders, tobacco control advocates, cancer association leaders, health ministries, and journalists. These meetings will reach across the entire breadth of cancer control and cancer care to focus energy and attention not just on talking about the cancer problem, but on identifying and sharing practical solutions that can make a lifesaving difference in communities around the world now.

Why is it so critical to unite the global cancer and tobacco control communities? Because, if your aim is to solve the cancer problem, the two are inseparable. The world is on a collision course if we fail to take action against the scourge of tobacco. Indeed, it's a train wreck not waiting to happen! Indeed, it's already happening and its repercussions will have a public health and economic impact unlike any we have ever experienced before.

As the only consumer product proven to kill more than half of its regular users, tobacco will be responsible for 4.9 million deaths worldwide this year alone. Today, that burden is almost evenly shared by industrialized and developing nations, but the trend is rapidly changing to the developing countries of the world.

If we fail to act to prevent this tragedy in the making, the consequences will most certainly be dire and destabilizing. As a direct result of tobacco use, at current rates, 650 million people alive today will eventually die, half of whom are now children. Half of these people will die in middle age—when they are most productive for their economies, their communities, and their families.

66   ISSUE 4 / Are We Winning the War on Cancer?

In the last century, tobacco use killed 100 million people. If left unchecked, tobacco use will kill more than one billion people in this century, and if we let it happen, it will be the worst case of avoidable loss of life in world history. Yet, we know with comprehensive, concerted action, we can eliminate the global scourge of tobacco and save hundreds of millions of lives within the next few decades, if we do the right things.

Let's take the United States as an example. We have enjoyed many resounding victories against Big Tobacco that are making a real difference toward the ultimate bottom line—lives saved. More than 2,200 communities nationwide have enacted smoke-free laws that are protecting the health of millions of Americans. In fact, tomorrow the Surgeon General will release the first report in 20 years focusing on secondhand smoke, and we expect it to confirm the public health and economic benefits of clean indoor air laws.

However, as smoking rates decline in the US and many other industrialized nations, the tobacco industry has dramatically stepped up its efforts in emerging markets. Because tobacco kills the majority of its customer base, the industry must persuade millions of people to become new smokers each year just to break even. In the largely unrestricted markets of the developing world, that means that no one is immune to the industry's tactics, especially the most vulnerable people of all—children.

Fortunately, thanks to the rigorous educational, scientific, and advocacy efforts of dedicated tobacco control activists worldwide, many nations are taking a stand against tobacco by supporting the world's first global public health treaty—the World Health Organization Framework Convention on Tobacco Control (FCTC). This treaty's evidence-based interventions have been proven to work in diverse cultures around the world.

The treaty hits the tobacco companies where they live by restricting their insidious and immoral marketing tactics. It gives nations—particularly the low-income nations the tobacco companies have targeted as their most promising markets—powerful new tools to protect their citizens from the tobacco industry's deception.

The US is to be commended for supporting adoption of the treaty, but our nation's role in this arena has been halted because we have so far refused to ratify it. As of June 20, 2006, 131 countries already have ratified the treaty, making it the most rapidly embraced treaty in UN history. Why are we lagging behind? The United States ratification and effective implementation of the treaty is essential to turning the tide of the global tobacco pandemic. To that end, I have urged President Bush to send the treaty to the Senate for ratification. And since many of the ratifying countries will be represented at the upcoming conferences, we will use that opportunity to bring pressure to bear on the administration and the US Senate to promptly join the rest of the world in ratifying the treaty. When ratified and implemented, we know from experience and evidence that human suffering will be reduced and lives will be saved.

In addition to taking immediate action against tobacco, there are three actions I believe it will take to eliminate cancer as a major public health problem at the earliest possible time.

First, we must accelerate discovery by redoubling and balancing our cancer research portfolio. Thanks to decades of well-funded, peer-reviewed research, cancer research has gone from a good bet to a sure bet. Remarkable achievements such as the mapping of the human genome make new cancer cures virtually inevitable, if we do the right things—and that is fully fund NIH and its National Cancer Institute. Further progress is guaranteed if research funding keeps pace. Landmark discoveries such as cancer vaccines and better and more targeted therapies are inevitable (assumed), but only if we fuel the engines of discovery. And we know that's what the American tax-payer and voter wants us to do!

And we must, at the same time, balance our research portfolio to include applied behavioral research, psychosocial and translational research, and evidence-based prevention interventions. If we redouble and balance cancer research efforts, the number of lives we could improve and save is unlimited over time. Unfortunately, funding for the NIH—the worldwide leader among cancer research institutions—is in jeopardy. If we fail to continue stoking the engines of research, we will effectively renege on our nation's commitment to the American people. And that's wrong!

Second, we must promote and elevate prevention into public policy and standard practice nationwide. One example of the enormous potential of prevention is cervical cancer. In nations like ours, where screening tests are available and early detection is standard practice, screening and follow-up treatment has reduced cervical cancer deaths by as much as 80 percent. And yet, despite these advances in prevention, in many parts of the world, cervical cancer is still a leading cause of cancer death in women.

As you know, recent FDA approval of the HPV vaccine, the first vaccine targeted specifically to preventing cancer, is one of the most important advances in women's health in recent decades. Successful global implementation of an effective HPV vaccine offers a truly unprecedented opportunity to prevent millions of deaths and dramatically reduce the world's cancer burden. The challenge is to make such advances available to every woman who needs them.

This is typical of the challenge facing cancer control advocates worldwide. Science has given us the tools to save lives, but our medical care and political systems are not equipped to deliver on those advances, which brings me to the third action.

Thirdly, we must drive delivery of state-of-the-art cancer care and control at the community level. In places where public health organizations, governments, and the private sector have worked together to drive delivery at the community level, there have been impressive results. With state-of-the-art cancer care, as many as 75 percent of cancer patients could survive long-term. Today, tragically, nowhere near this many will receive treatment that fully takes advantage of what science has taught us.

Access to the means for the attainment and preservation of health is a basic human need and right and should not be thought of as a privilege for just the few.

If we fail to do the right things, it will not only result in an otherwise avoidable public health catastrophe, but also an economic missed opportunity. For example, here in the US, a 20% reduction in cancer mortality will yield a

10 trillion dollar value to the American people, according to a study done by Kevin M. Murphy and Robert H. Topel entitled The Economic Value of Medical Research.

Because cancer tends to strike and kill in the prime of one's life, its human and economic impact is difficult to exaggerate. Truly, a nation's very competitiveness in the future will be tied to how healthy its citizens are.

So the underlying key to achieving each of these goals is advocacy. Cancer is as much a political and public policy issue as it is a medical and public health issue. Remarkable advances in prevention, early detection, and treatment virtually guarantee lower incidence and mortality rates—if they are available to everyone who needs them.

That means our most pressing challenge is to make cancer a policy priority—to educate lawmakers, governments, and civic leaders about the urgency of cancer control and inspire their commitment to enact public policies that will make cancer advances available to all people everywhere.

Obviously, this is an enormously complicated task, but we need only look to advocacy successes here in the United States to see the remarkable, lifesaving potential of public policy solutions to the world's public health problems.

Let me cite one contemporary example. Recently, the American Cancer Society Cancer Action Network (ACS CAN)—the Society's sister 501(c)4 advocacy organization—took action against the small business health care legislation known as "Health Insurance Marketplace Modernization and Affordability Act," or S. 1955, which would have effectively gutted state laws that require health insurers to cover lifesaving cancer screenings and treatments.

Working with our partners—AARP and the American Diabetes Association—ACS CAN launched a multi-media advertising campaign that received an immediate, strong response from grassroots volunteers. More than 170,000 emails poured into US Senate offices and nearly 10,000 calls came in from constituents requesting to be connected to the target Senate offices. I'm proud to report that our collaborative efforts were successful. On May 12, the bill was stopped in the US Senate.

But, although we've made extraordinary progress, we still have a long way to go.

That's why ACS CAN is planning to bring 10,000 energetic advocates representing every congressional district in the country to Capitol Hill this September 19 and 20 for Celebration on the Hill to meet with their elected officials and participate in activities on the National Mall with an important message: "We care about cancer, and we will be heard. We will do our part, but you must do yours. And we will not take 'no' for an answer." Cancer survivors don't take life and health for granted—and they vote with their feet and voices as well as their ballots.

Our ability to make a difference in the lives of people touched by cancer increases exponentially when we help pass laws and establish public policies that secure investments in research and prevention, and access to quality health care.

Ultimately, the challenge for all of us will be to do what we can to redouble our efforts in pursuit of our common cancer-fighting agenda. This means

YES / John R. Seffrin   **69**

we must have the courage to share, the courage to take responsible, bold risks, and the courage to persevere. In other words, we must have the courage to transform what is into what could be.

In conclusion, I leave you with the following truth: When the American Cancer Society was founded in 1913, a diagnosis of cancer was a virtual death sentence only to be preceded by an often protracted period of pain and suffering. Due to an indefatigable commitment to research and intervention at the community level, cancer has been transformed and is today potentially the most preventable and most curable of the major life-threatening diseases facing humankind.

We now have the knowledge and know-how to turn that potentiality into reality, if we do the right things. And may God speed that day.

Thank you.

Reynold Spector    **NO**

The War on Cancer: A Progress Report for Skeptics

In 1971, President Nixon and Congress declared war on cancer. Since then, the federal government has spent well over $105 billion on the effort. What have we gained from that huge investment? David Nathan, a well-known professor and administrator, maintains in his book *The Cancer Treatment Revolution* (Wiley, 2007) that we have made substantial progress. However, he greatly overestimates the potential of the newer so-called "smart drugs." Researchers Psyrri and De Vita (2008) also claim important progress. However, they cherry-pick the cancers with which there has been some progress and do not discuss the failures. Moreover, they only discuss the last decade rather than a more balanced view of 1950 or 1975 to the present.

On the other hand, Gina Kolata pointed out in *The New York Times* that the cancer death rate, adjusted for the size and age of the population, has decreased by only 5 percent since 1950. She argues that there has been very little overall progress in the war on cancer.

In this article, I will focus on adult cancer, since child cancer makes up less than 1 percent of all cancer diagnosed. I will then place the facts in proper perspective after an overview of the epidemiology, diagnosis, and treatment (especially with smart drugs) of adult cancer in the United States.

The Cancer Facts

Summary statistics show that the war on cancer has not gone well. This is in marked contrast to death rates from stroke and cardiovascular disease (adjusted for the age and size of the population), which have fallen by 74 percent and 64 percent, respectively, from 1950 through 2006; and by 60 percent and 52 percent, respectively, from 1975 through 2006. These excellent results against stroke and heart disease are mainly due to improvements in drug therapy, especially the control of high blood pressure to prevent stroke and the use of statins, aspirin, beta blockers, calcium channel blockers, and ACE inhibitors (now all generic) to prevent and treat heart disease. Cancer therapy is clearly decades behind. However, these data conceal a great deal of useful information and do not provide guidance on how to make progress against cancer.

Figure 1

U.S. Mortality, 2006

Rank	Cause of Death	No. of Deaths	% of All Deaths
1.	Heart Diseases	631,636	26.0
2.	Cancer	559,888	23.1
3.	Cerebrovascular Diseases	137,119	5.7
4.	Chronic Lower Respiratory Diseases	124,583	5.1
5.	Accidents (unintentional injuries)	121,599	5.0
6.	Diabetes Mellitus	72,449	3.0
7.	Alzheimer Disease	72,432	3.0
8.	Influenza & Pneumonia	56,326	2.3
9.	Nephritis*	45,344	1.9
10.	Septicemia	34,234	1.4

*Includes nephrotic syndrome and nephrosis.
Sources: U.S. Mortality Data 2006, National Health and Statistics, Centers for Disease Control and Prevention, 2009

Methodological Issues

To understand the issues, we must describe a few statistical traps and define our terms (see table 1). For example, there are several types of detection bias. First, if one discovers a malignant tumor very early and starts therapy immediately, even if the therapy is worthless, it will appear that the patient lives longer than a second patient (with an identical tumor) treated with another worthless drug if the cancer in the second patient was detected later. Second, detection bias can also occur with small tumors, especially of the breast and prostate, that would not harm the patient if left untreated but can lead to

Table 1

Critical Terms Defined in the Text

1. Cancer—three kinds: local, regional, distant (metastatic)
2. Carcinoma (cancer) in situ—e.g., ductal carcinoma of the breast (DCIS)
3. Slow cancers—e.g., prostate, breast
4. Cancer treatments: surgery, chemotherapy, radiation therapy
5. Partial response
6. Complete response
7. Cure
8. Median survival, one/five-year survival

72 ISSUE 4 / Are We Winning the War on Cancer?

Figure 2

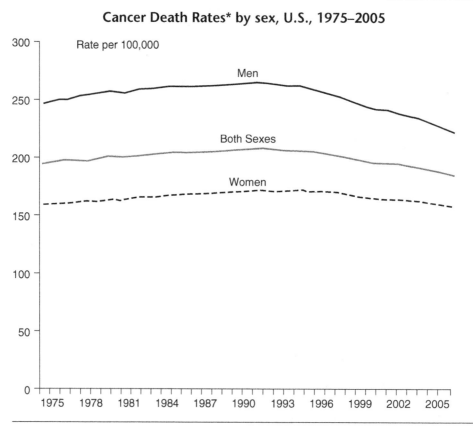

Cancer Death Rates* by sex, U.S., 1975–2005

*Age-adjusted to the U.S. 2000 standard population.

Sources: U.S. Mortality Data 2006, National Health and Statistics, Centers for Disease Control and Prevention, 2008

unnecessary and sometimes mutilating therapy. Another type is publication bias, whereby positive studies (especially those funded by the pharmaceutical industry) tend to be published while negative studies do not.

What is cancer? Cancer is a large group of diseases characterized by the uncontrolled growth and spread of abnormal cells locally, regionally, and/or distantly (metastatically). A carcinoma (cancer) in situ is a small cancer that has not invaded the local tissue. Some cancers grow very slowly, and the patient may survive for ten years or more with minimal treatment. Other cancers (e.g., lung and pancreas) grow quickly and, even today, kill more than half of the patients in less than one year (see table 2). The therapy for cancer is generally surgery, if possible, and/or chemotherapy and/or radiation therapy. Chemotherapy aims to kill the cancer cells, but most chemotherapeutic drugs are nonspecific and also kill sensitive normal cells, especially in the intestine and bone marrow. Radiation therapy is also nonspecific. In chemotherapy

NO / Reynold Spector   **73**

Table 2

Common Cancers Current Death and Survival Statistics (American Cancer Society 2009)

Cancer Origin	Percent of Cancer Deaths	One-Year Survival (%)	Five-Year Survival (%)
Lung	28	41	15
Colon/Rectum	9	83	64
Breast	8	>95	89
Pancreas	6	24	5
Prostate	5	*	*
Leukemia	4	**	51
Lymphoma	4	82	68
Liver	3	†	<10
Other	33	‡	‡

*Survival statistics for prostate cancer are very misleading since they include many treated cancers that would not have harmed (or killed) the patient (see test).

**Leukemia is a heterogenous group of diseases. The five-year survival figure is an average of all types.

†Liver cancer is a rapidly fatal disease in which treatment is ineffective.

‡Other cancers are so heterogenous that the reader should consult the American Cancer Society (2009) for specific data.

and radiation therapy, a partial response is defined as shrinkage of the tumor in each dimension by 50 percent; a complete response means no detectable tumor, but this does not necessarily mean a "cure." Many complete responses are only transitory. Median survival is the length of time in which one-half of the patients in a cohort die.

What Do We Know About Cancer?

The "causes" of cancer are shown in table 3, though there is still much we don't know. For example, we do not know exactly how smoking causes cancer; in most cases, we do not know how "acquired" mutations cause cancer. In some cancers, there are more than five hundred identifiable genetic abnormalities— no one knows which one(s), if any, is "causative." The importance of epigenetic changes is currently speculative. It is quite possible that there is a completely unknown causal mechanism in many cancers.

The diagnosis of cancer today is relatively straightforward with imaging techniques (x-ray, CAT, MRI, PET) and biopsies that are subjected to routine histology, electron microscopy, and immunological techniques.

74   ISSUE 4 / Are We Winning the War on Cancer?

Table 3

**Examples of Probable or Definite Causes of Cancer
(American Cancer Society 2009)**

1. External Factors
   a. Tobacco
   b. Chemicals (e.g., asbestos, benzene, alcohol)
   c. Radiation
   d. Infections, organisms (e.g., hepatitis B, papilloma virus, *Helicobacter*)
   e. Hormone replacement therapy with estrogen
2. Inernal Factors
   a. Genetic mutations
       1) inherited
       2) acquired
   b. Hormones (e.g., estrogen)
   c. Immune disorders (e.g., AIDS)
   d. Epigenetic changes
   e. Obesity

Table 4

**Criteria for Utility of Cancer Therapy
(Fojo and Grady 2009)**

1. Meaningful prolongation of life or cure (mortality)
2. Improvement of quality of life (symptoms)
3. Value of treatment (compared to cost)

Cancer Therapy

To have a reasonable discussion of cancer therapy, we need to agree on the objectives of therapy, as shown in table 4. Everyone agrees that meaningful prolongation of life, preferably complete surgical removal of the tumor and cure, is a high priority. The treatment should also improve the quality of life. But, as is well known, many chemotherapeutic and radiation regimens cause mild to devastating—even fatal—side effects. Nathan (2007) compares conventional chemotherapy to "carpet-bombing," an extreme but realistic metaphor. Finally, the results of a cost-benefit analysis must be reasonable. (In some cases, justifiably and importantly, chemotherapy and/or radiation and/or other drugs are used as palliative measures exclusively to counter symptoms from the disease [e.g., pleural effusions in the chest cavity or bone pain] or from the treatments [e.g., vomiting, mucositis, low white blood counts, heart failure, nerve damage, diarrhea, and/or inflammation of the bladder]). In the final analysis, what counts are the criteria in table 4. Partial or even complete remissions, unless they prolong life and/or improve the overall quality of life at a reasonable cost, are scientifically interesting but of little use to the patient.

Currently there are a few metastatic cancers that can sometimes be cured with chemotherapy and/or radiation therapy, but unfortunately these cures make up a very small percentage of the whole cancer problem. These cancers include testicular cancer, choriocarcinoma, Hodgkin's and non-Hodgkin's lymphoma, leukemia, and rare cases of breast and ovarian cancer. A few cancers can be made into chronic diseases that require daily treatment, e.g., chronic myelogenous leukemia.

Returning to table 2, lung cancer, the most common cancer, is a devastating disease; if the surgeon cannot totally remove it, the diagnosis is grim. In fact, about 60 percent of lung cancer patients are dead within one year of diagnosis with the best available therapy, and only 15 percent survive five years.

There has been some progress in the death rate from colorectal cancer, especially in women. This is mainly due to earlier diagnosis and surgical therapy.

Cancer of the breast is often a slow cancer and has a five- to ten-year median survival rate with just surgical therapy. There has been a modest decline in death rates from breast cancer since 1975. It is worth noting that currently, if the breast cancer is metastatic, five-year survival is only 27 percent. However, breast cancer presents a serious dilemma. Early detection of invasive breast cancer by screening is good; however, about 62,000 cases of ductal carcinoma in situ (DCIS) are also discovered every year. In greater than 50 percent of these women, especially older women, these lesions will not progress and do not need treatment. However, it is difficult to predict who will not need therapy, so the American Cancer Society (2009) recommends all patients with DCIS undergo therapy—generally breast surgery. Thus, more than thirty thousand patents annually are unnecessarily treated. We need to figure out which DCIS are harmless in order to avoid unnecessary treatment. On balance, I feel that breast cancer screening has a small but positive net benefit.

Pancreatic cancer is devastating (see table 2), and little progress has been made against it since 1975. Pancreatic cancer is very challenging because the tumors are surrounded by dense fibrous connective tissue with few blood vessels. Because of this, it is difficult to deliver drugs to pancreatic tumors. Moreover, this explains in part why chemotherapy is so ineffective for pancreatic cancer (see table 2). Better animal models are needed.

Prostate cancer mortality has declined slightly since 1975 with an unexplained increase in the mid-1990s. But prostate cancer therapy also presents a serious quandary. At autopsy, approximately 30 percent (or more) of men have cancer foci in their prostate glands, yet only 1 to 2 percent of men die of prostate cancer. Thus less than 10 percent of prostate cancer patients require treatment. This presents a serious dilemma: whom should the physician treat? Moreover, recently, two large studies of prostate cancer screening with prostate specific antigen (PSA) have seriously questioned the utility of screening. In one study, the investigators had to screen over a thousand men before they saved one life. This led to about fifty "false positive" patients who often underwent surgery and/or radiation therapy unnecessarily. The second study, conducted in the United States, was negative, i.e., no lives were saved due to the screening, but many of the screening-positive patients with prostate cancer were treated. Welch and Albertson (2009) and Brawley (2009) estimate that more than a million men in the U.S. have been unnecessarily treated for prostate cancer between 1986 and 2005, due to over-diagnostic PSA screening tests. In the end, screening for prostate cancer will not be useful until methods are developed to determine which prostate cancers detected by screening will harm the patient. Many men—especially elderly ones—with a histological diagnosis of prostate cancer elect "watchful waiting" with no therapy, a rational strategy.

There are many other things we do not understand about cancer—even on a phenomenological level. For example, in the United States, the incidence and death rates from cancer of the stomach have fallen dramatically since 1930. The reason for this is unknown but may be due to changes in food preservation; it is not due to treatment.

Smart Drugs

David Nathan (2007) extols the virtues and potential of the new "smart drugs." Smart drugs are defined as drugs that focus on a particular vulnerability of the cancer; they are not generalized but rather specific toxins. But the *Journal of the American Medical Association* reports that 90 percent of the drugs or biologics approved by the FDA in the past four years for cancer (many of them smart drugs) cost more than $20,000 for twelve weeks of therapy, and many offer a survival benefit of only two months or less. Let us take bevacizumab (Avastin), the ninth largest selling drug in America ($4.8 billion in 2008), costing about $8,000 per month per patient. Bevacizumab, a putative smart drug, is an intravenous man-made antibody that blocks the action of vascular endothelial growth factor (VEFG). It sometimes works because tumors (and normal tissues) release VEFG to facilitate small blood vessel in-growth into the tumor. These small blood vessels "nourish" the tumor (or normal tissue). The idea is to "starve" the growing tumor with once or twice monthly intravenous injections of bevacizumab.

The FDA has approved bevacizumab for the cancers listed in table 5. Since the median survival of colorectal cancer is eighteen months, bevacizumab therapy would cost about $144,000 (in such a patient) for four months prolongation of survival. In the other cancers in table 4, there is no prolongation of survival. Moreover, bevacizumab can have terrible side effects, including gastrointestinal perforations, serious bleeding, severe hypertension, clot formation, and delayed wound healing. By the criteria in table 4, bevacizumab is at best a marginal drug. It only slightly prolongs life, demonstrable only in colorectal cancer, has serious side effects, and is very expensive.

Bevacizumab is frequently cited as an example of the so-called newer smart drugs. But by interfering with small blood vessel growth throughout the body, it is a nonspecific toxin—and hence has serious side effects. It is not so different from the older non-specific chemotherapy.

The use of bevacizumab and similar drugs raises another issue. According to Gina Kolata, 60 to 80 percent of oncologists' revenue comes from infusion

NO / Reynold Spector   **77**

Table 5

Bevacizumab (Avastin)—Utility

Cancer	Evidence for Prolongation of Life; time*
Bowel/Rectum	Yes, four months (median survival) with other drugs
Lung	No +
Breast	No
Kidney	No
Glioblastoma (Brain)	No

*Compared to randomized control (if available).

+"No" means a lack of a statistically significant prolongation.

of anti-cancer drugs in their offices. Many believe that such economic incentives are the reason for the substantial overuse of expensive chemotherapeutic drugs. However, it is very difficult to document the extent of the overuse of cancer chemotherapy. Does it make sense to employ such expensive drugs that do not prolong life (see table 5) and have such serious side effects? Moreover, although VEGF and bevacizumab are interesting science, there has been gross exaggeration of bevacizumab's clinical utility in the press (see tables 4 and 5).

So why does the U.S. Food and Drug Administration (FDA) approve bevacizumab (and other drugs) that do not improve longevity and/or the quality of life (see table 5)? The answer is that bevacizumab coupled with other drugs can cause partial remissions, "stabilization" of the cancer, or "lack of progression" for several months. However, this often does not lead to prolongation of life in most of the cancers in table 5. Moreover, many patients pay a heavy price in terms of side effects and cost. It is also worth noting that several European national regulatory authorities do not accept the utility of some of these smart drugs and do not license them for sale in their countries. In agreement with the Europeans, scientists at the U.S. National Cancer Institute are urging the oncology community, regulators, and the public to set limits on the use and pricing of such marginal drugs. They view the current situation as unsustainable.

Why Has the War on Cancer Failed?

As documented above, unlike the successes against heart disease and stroke, the war on cancer, after almost forty years, must be deemed a failure with a few notable exceptions. Why? Is it because cancer is an incredibly tough problem, or are there other explanations? In table 6, I have listed six reasons for the failure, although there is little doubt that effective, safe therapy of the various cancers is a difficult problem.

Table 6

Why Has the War on Cancer Failed?

1. We don't understand the cause/pathogenesis in most case of cancer—smoking is an obvious phenomenological exception.
2. Most treatments (except surgery) are nonspecific cell killers and not "smart."
3. Clinical trials and the grant system don't foster innovation—need reform.
4. Screening for useful drugs against cancer cells has not worked.
5. Animal models of cancer are often inadequate—e.g., pancreatic cancer as described in this article.
6. Unproductive "facts" in research come and go.

Where Should We Go from Here?

In my view the principal problem is that we just do not understand the causes of most cancers. We don't even know if the problem is genetic or epigenetic or something totally unknown. In theory, problems 2 through 6 in table 6 are all correctable with political and scientific will and more knowledge. Even though we know cancer of the lung is caused by cigarette smoking, we do not know the mechanism, and (except for surgery) we do not know how to meaningfully intervene (see table 2). The pharmaceutical industry cannot make real progress until we understand the mechanisms and molecular causes of cancer so that industrial, academic, and governmental scientists have rational targets for intervention. We will make no progress if there are five hundred or more genetic abnormalities in a single cancer cell. Where would one begin?

What Should We Do Now?

We can still do a lot even today (see table 7). Smoking and hormone replacement therapy are a cause of lung and breast cancer, respectively, and should be stopped or minimized. For hepatitis B (which causes over 50 percent of liver cancer) and papilloma virus (which causes almost all cervical cancer and some anal and mouth cancers), we can vaccinate with vaccines that are essentially 100 percent effective. *Helicobacter* (the probable cause of some stomach cancer) can be easily eliminated with antibiotics. Prophylactic finasteride and tamoxifen (both generic) can decrease prostate and breast cancer, respectively (in high risk patients). We must also decrease alcohol intake (liver and esophageal cancer) and obesity. Obesity is associated with increased cancer risk but the mechanism, if causal, is obscure.

We can screen for cervical, colorectal, and breast cancer, although the value of breast cancer screening is not clear (due to overdiagnosis), as I discussed above. However, in my view, the benefit of breast cancer screening slightly outweighs the harm. For example, if DCIS treatment could be rationalized and provided only to those who need it, breast cancer screening would

NO / Reynold Spector   **79**

Table 7

The Way Forward

1. Prevention (cancer prevented)
   a. Stop smoking (lung; others)
   b. Minimize hormone replacement therapy (breast)
   c. Vaccines
      1) Hepatitis B (liver)
      2) Papilloma virus (cervical, anal, penis)
   d. Eliminate *Helicobacter* with antibiotics (stomach)
   e. Prevent contracting AIDS (sarcoma)
   f. Chemoprophylaxis
      3) finasteride (prostate)
      4) tamoxifen (high risk breast)
   g. Decrease alcohol (liver, esophagus)
   h. Decrease obesity (many types)
2. Screening for
   a. Cervical cancer
   b. Colorectal cancer
   c. Breast cancer
3. More knowledge of cancers' causes and better animal models
4. Better drugs—once appropriate targets identified

---

then be unarguably useful. All attempts to screen for lung cancer, even in smokers, have so far been futile.

If all these recommendations were followed, we could cut cancer deaths in half. Moreover, with better mechanistic understanding of cancer, we could make truly "smart" drugs, as has been done in recent years for atherosclerosis (heart attacks), hypertension (strokes), gastrointestinal diseases (ulcers), and AIDS—with truly remarkable results. Let us hope cancer is next.

POSTSCRIPT

Are We Winning the War on Cancer?

Although many diseases have similar or worse outcomes, cancer is generally more feared than heart disease or diabetes. Cancer is regarded as a disease that must be "battled" and a "war" on cancer has been declared. Fighting or military-like descriptions are often used to address cancer's human effects, and they emphasize the need for the patient to take immediate, decisive actions himself or herself, rather than to delay, ignore, or rely on others caring for him or her.

Forty years ago, talk therapy to change a patient's outlook on life was a relatively popular alternative cancer treatment. It was based on the idea that cancer was caused by a negative personality or attitude. People with a "cancer personality"—depressed, repressed, self-hating, and unable to express their emotions—were believed to have developed cancer through their personality and/or their attitudes. This theory allowed society to blame the victim for having developed cancer or having prevented its cure by their negative attitude and personality. It also increased patients' anxieties as they incorrectly believe that natural emotions of sadness, anger, or fear either gave them the disease or prevented them from being cured. The author Susan Sontag helped promote this idea in her book *Illness as Metaphor* written in 1978 while recovering from treatment for breast cancer. Although the idea of personality causing cancer has not been supported by research, the belief that thinking positively will increase survival, especially among breast cancer patients, is common. An article "Invited Commentary: Personality as a Causal Factor in Cancer Risk and Mortality—Time to Retire a Hypothesis?" in the *American Journal of Epidemiology* (2010) reports findings from a large-scale study of the value of two personality dimensions, neuroticism and extraversion, for cancer risk and life expectancy. Overall, no relationship was found between personality and cancer onset or survival. The authors question whether it is time for the field to move on from considering a role for personality in cancer to more promising and modifiable factors.

For further information on the progress of the war on cancer, see "Declining Death Rates Reflect Progress Against Cancer," *PLoS ONE* (2010). The article discusses the success of the "war on cancer" initiated in 1971. The authors found that death rate for all cancers combined in men showed a net decline of 21 percent and 11 percent from the 1990 and 1970 rates, respectively. Similarly, the all-cancer death rate in women showed a net decline of 12 percent and 6 percent from the 1991 and 1970 rates, respectively. These decreases since 1990–91 translate to preventing of 561,400 cancer deaths in men and 205,700 deaths in women. The decrease in death rates from all cancers involved all ages and racial/ethnic groups. The positive change in cancer death rates since 1990 resulted mostly from reductions in smoking, increased screening allowing early detection of several cancers, and improvements in treatment for specific cancers. Although much overall progress has been made in cancer treatment and prevention, lung cancer remains a difficult disease to treat with generally poor prognoses. In "Lung Cancer: Progress in Diagnosis, Staging and Therapy," *Respirology* (January 2010), the authors indicate that lung cancer remains one of the greatest medical challenges with nearly 1.5 million new cases world-wide each year and a growing tobacco epidemic in the developing world. The value of screening for early disease is not yet established and trials to see if mortality can be improved as a result are in progress. For further reading, see "Two Decades of Declining Cancer Mortality: Progress with Disparity," *Annual Review of Public Health* (2010). In this article, the authors claim that despite considerable progress in preventing and treating cancer, disparities in cancer mortality persist across different races and social classes. Because all the factors that account for declining cancer trends are related to social class, and because of large social class disparities in cancer risk factors, there will likely be a widening gap in cancer deaths among those in lower socioeconomic groups in the future.

Also see the following: "Breast Cancer—A Voyage into Hearts and Minds," *Psychologist* (February 2011); "Cancer," *Time* (February 14, 2011); "Fighting Cancer Takes on a New Dimension," *Chronicle of Philanthropy* (January 13, 2011); and "Not Just an Illness of the Rich," *Scientific American* (March 2011).

ISSUE 3

Can an Overemphasis on Eating Healthy Become Unhealthy?

YES: Lindsey Getz, from "Orthorexia: When Eating Healthy Becomes an Unhealthy Obsession," *Today's Dietitian* (June 2009)

NO: Chris Woolston, from "What's Wrong With the American Diet?" *Consumer Health Interactive* (October 28, 2009)

As you read the issue, focus on the following points:

1. The messages that professional health and nutrition associations, government agencies like USDA, and registered dietitians promote about healthy eating.
2. What orthorexia is and what causes the condition.
3. How "healthy eating" messages may lead to orthorexia.
4. The differences between orthorexia nervosa and anorexia nervosa.
5. How to recognize a person with symptoms of orthorexia and the recommended treatment for the condition.

ISSUE SUMMARY

YES: Writer Lindsey Getz describes orthorexia, the condition that makes a person strive for a perfect diet. People with orthorexia avoid sugar, trans fat, cholesterol, sodium, and anything they believe is "unhealthy" and take pride in eating a perfect diet.

NO: Health and medical writer Chris Woolston believes the typical American diet is excessive in calories, fat, and sugar. He says we would be much healthier if we ate more "fish, poultry, cruciferous vegetables (i.e., cabbage and broccoli), greens, tomatoes, legumes, fresh fruits, and whole grains." He also believes we should "skimp on fatty or calorie-rich foods such as red meats, eggs, high-fat dairy products, french fries, pizza, mayonnaise, candy, and desserts."

T he mid-1970s was the birth of the "negative nutrition" era when people were told certain foods are bad and to avoid eating them. During this time, reports hit the news telling people that foods high in saturated fat and cholesterol cause heart disease; sugary foods increase chances of getting diabetes and cause cavities; salt increases blood pressure; and artificial flavors and coloring increase the risk of cancer.

Adding to the negativism, the *U.S. Dietary Goals for Americans* were developed in 1977, and 3 years later, the first *Dietary Guidelines for Americans* were published. Both convey messages telling us not to eat certain foods. At the same time, organizations like the American Heart Association and American Cancer Society published dietary recommendations with similar messages.

The organic food movement began in the late 1970s and has increased dramatically since then, especially after the passage of the Organic Food Production Act of 1990. Proponents of organic foods say that it's better than conventionally grown foods since pesticides in conventionally grown products cause health problems.

Today, we are bombarded with messages that tell us to eat better. Web sites, newsletters, and newspaper columns are dedicated to the "right" way to eat. Magazine covers stress healthy eating: and there's even one called *EatingWell*. The Web address for the American Dietetic Association says it all, "*http://www.eatright.org.*"

In 1997, after years of working with patients who were obsessed with healthy diets, physician Steven Bratman wrote the article "The Health Food Eating Disorder" (*Yoga Journal*, October 1997). In the article, he describes a new condition where people are obsessed with healthy foods. He outlines his definition and description as follows:

> Many of the most unbalanced people I have ever met are those who have devoted themselves to healthy eating. In fact, I believe some of them have actually contracted a novel eating disorder for which I have coined the name "orthorexia nervosa." The term uses "ortho," meaning straight, correct, and true, to modify "anorexia nervosa." Orthorexia nervosa refers to a pathological fixation on eating proper food.
>
> Orthorexia begins, innocently enough, as a desire to overcome chronic illness or to improve general health. But because it requires considerable willpower to adopt a diet that differs radically from the food habits of childhood and the surrounding culture, few accomplish the change gracefully. Most must resort to an iron self-discipline bolstered by a hefty dose of superiority over those who eat junk food. Over time, what to eat, how much, and the consequences of dietary indiscretion come to occupy a greater and greater proportion of the orthorexic's day.

Orthorexia is not considered a medically defined eating disorder by the American Psychiatric Association (APA). Tim Walsh, who led the group of psychiatrists that worked on the 2013 edition of APA'S *DSM*, a manual, told *Time* magazine (February 12, 2010) that it will not be included in it.

"We're not in a position to say it doesn't exist or it's not important," Walsh told *Time* magazine (February 12, 2010). "The real issue is significant data. Getting listed as a separate entry in the *DSM* requires extensive scientific knowledge of a syndrome and broad clinical acceptance, neither of which orthorexia has."

More research about orthorexia has been conducted in Europe than in the United States. Donini and colleagues published a report in *Eating and Weight Disorders* (June 2004) where they found that 6.9 percent of 400 Italians have this condition.

Many nutritionists and other health professionals believe that it is a true disorder. So what has caused the condition? Have the messages to improve our eating caused some people to eat too healthful? Lindsey Getz describes orthorexia as a real condition that dietitians should be concerned about. Christina Pirello considers it to be the "most ridiculous disorder that the psychiatric industry has fabricated."

TIMELINE

1977 *U.S. Dietary Goals* are published that recommend limiting fat to 30 percent of total caloric intake.

1979 The first *Healthy People: The Surgeon General's Report on Health Promotion and Disease Prevention* is published.

1980 First *Dietary Guidelines for Americans* is published that recommended limiting fat, sugar, and sodium.

1990 Organic Food Production Act is passed.

1997 "Orthorexia" is first defined by Steven Bratman.

2006 The Alliance for a Healthier Generation and the American Beverage Association agree to eliminate high-calorie soft drinks from public schools by 2009–2010.

DEFINITIONS

Diagnostic and Statistical Manual of Mental Disorders (DSM) Manual published by the American Psychiatric Association that defines various mental disorders.

"Negative Nutrition" Harmful foods and practices.

Obsessive-compulsive disorder (OCD) Anxiety disorder characterized by recurrent unwanted thoughts (obsessions) and/or repetitive behaviors (compulsions).

Orthos Greek word meaning "correct or right."

Orexis Greek word meaning "appetite."

Orthorexia A fixation of eating only pure, healthy, and natural foods.

YES ⬅   Lindsey Getz

Orthorexia: When Eating Healthy Becomes an Unhealthy Obsession

*T*here's a fine line between including foods deemed healthy in your diet and eating nothing but! Teaching your clients the value of all foods can help them forge a healthy relationship with eating and may prevent them from taking their diet to a potentially dangerous extreme.

What could be wrong with a desire to eat healthy? After all, promoting healthy eating is part of a dietitian's job description. But when the urge to eat healthy foods becomes more of an obsession, there may be an eating disorder in the works—and the consequences can be dangerous.

Although it is not yet a clinically recognized term or disorder, orthorexia is gaining wider recognition as cases continue to emerge and capture media attention. Steven Bratman, MD, author of *Health Food Junkies—Orthorexia Nervosa: Overcoming the Obsession With Healthful Eating*, coined the term to denote an eating disorder characterized by an obsession with eating foods deemed healthy.

Bratman began studying the condition after personally becoming obsessed with health foods. "I suffered from a psychological obsession with food," he said in a *20/20* interview last year. "When I was involved with this, it took up way too much of my life experiences when there were other things I could have been doing."

Like other eating disorders, orthorexia starts to negatively impact many areas of an individual's life and, in some cases, can even lead to severe malnutrition or death, as the person increasingly eliminates food types from his or her diet.

"It's not an official diagnostic term, but I think it's something that's important for dietitians to know about," says Evelyn Tribole, MS, RD, owner of a California-based nutrition counseling practice and author of seven books, including *Healthy Homestyle Cooking* and *Intuitive Eating*. "If a client likes to always eat healthy, the question is whether it's helping or hurting them. Is it something that affects their social life? For instance, are they no longer seeing their friends because they can't go out to dinner? This is the type of indication that eating healthy is becoming an unhealthy obsession."

Orthorexia could easily begin as simple healthy habits but then spiral out of control, adds Sondra Kronberg, MS, RD, CDN, a national liaison for the

40   ISSUE 3 / Can an Overemphasis on Eating Healthy Become . . . ?

National Eating Disorders Association and the cofounder and nutritional director of the Eating Disorder Associates Treatment & Referral Centers and Eating Wellness Programs of New York. "The person takes something that's normally considered healthy and good for their body and takes it to the extreme," she says. "They wind up with disordered thinking and psychological torment. The behavior becomes restrictive to the degree that it begins to interfere with the person's quality of life. And what starts out as something they are controlling becomes something that controls them."

Unlike anorexia or bulimia, orthorexia is not about the desire to become thin. "The driving force seems to be a desire to eat a perfectly healthy or even 'pure' diet," says Deborah Kauffmann, RD, LDN, owner of Mindfulness Based Nutrition Counseling in Baltimore. "For instance, organically grown vegetables and fruits may be thought of as 'safe foods' [for both those with anorexia and orthorexia] because they are seen as healthy and low in calories. But artificial sweeteners and diet frozen meals, which usually seem acceptable to someone with anorexia, would not be seen as acceptable to someone with orthorexic tendencies. Conversely, expeller-pressed canola oil may be acceptable to someone with orthorexia but not someone with anorexia because of the fear of weight gain due to eating fat."

Impressionable Minds

Perhaps one of the most alarming trends associated with orthorexia is that children are picking up some of these tendencies. Kids who watch their parents obsess over certain foods may mimic that behavior. And well-intentioned parents who strictly limit their children's sugar intake or try to feed them only organic foods may instill a sense of fear in their children that other foods are "bad" or that scary things could happen if they eat them.

"A few years ago, I had a 10 year old who was terrified of trans fats," says Tribole. "Part of her treatment was me sitting down and eating a Ding Dong with her. Can you imagine a dietitian eating a Ding Dong with her client? But she needed a healthier relationship with food. She had to realize that you don't eat one Ding Dong and end up with a clogged artery."

"I believe many well-meaning parents, teachers, pediatricians, and even dietitians are passing on their beliefs about unhealthy foods to children," says Kauffmann. "This can create not only orthorexia but eating disorders like anorexia, bulimia, and compulsive eating. Recently, I have seen children in my practice afraid to eat all kinds of foods because of things they have learned at home or in school regarding foods being unhealthy or fattening. In my practice, I often use the program in the book *Preventing Childhood Eating Problems* [*A Practical, Positive Approach to Raising Children Free of Food & Weight Conflicts*] by Jane Hirschmann and Lela Zaphiropoulos to teach parents how to help their children become healthy, intuitive eaters. Parents also need to understand that healthy bodies come in all shapes and sizes. Ellyn Satter's book *Your Child's Weight: Helping Without Harming* includes a wonderful appendix which reviews the literature regarding the actual relationship between weight and health in children."

Parents must be especially careful with the behavior they exhibit around their kids and also keep an eye on whether they are too involved with their children's diet, says D. Milton Stokes, MPH, RD, CDN, owner of One Source Nutrition, LLC in Connecticut. Parents can easily make the transition from being helpful and healthy to giving their children a complex about what they're eating. "Kids have a natural appetite regulation," says Stokes. "They eat when they're hungry and stop when they're full. That gets interrupted when mom starts pushing more or less food. Everyone should rely more on that physiological hunger rather than turning eating into something emotional."

Developing a healthy relationship with food certainly seems to be a key to preventing these tendencies, and that means not tying words with heavy meaning to food. "In our society, food is constantly painted as this moral dilemma," says Tribole. "A low-fat food may be termed 'guilt free,' for instance. But eating shouldn't make you feel guilty. And we are constantly calling foods 'good' or 'bad.' Putting all of this weight onto what we eat, as though it actually affects who you are as a person, is where the problem is stemming from. And kids pick up on that."

Instead, parents should teach their children about moderation. Frequently eating trans fatty foods such as French fries or processed snacks is not healthy behavior, but neither is becoming obsessive about avoiding them or being scared to be around such foods.

Warning Signs

Because orthorexia is not an officially recognized disorder and is somewhat controversial, many dietitians may be unfamiliar with it. Some physicians and other health professionals say orthorexia does not require its own classification because they believe it is a form of anorexia or obsessive-compulsive disorder.

Still, regardless of what orthorexia is called or how it is classified, dietitians should be aware of potential warning signs that could indicate something is wrong with the way a client views and eats food. The "worry factor" is one of the biggest indicators, suggests Tribole. "If a client has too much anxiety over what they eat, then that stress may be worse for their health than what they're actually eating and can lead to these orthorexic tendencies," she says.

If you have a client who follows a particularly restrictive diet, try to gain a sense of their feelings about food and whether they're behaving obsessively. "In other words, if they go to a party and they're only serving fried foods, are they going to be devastated? Are they not going to eat all night? These are signs that their behavior is extreme," warns Tribole.

"Also look for any patterns that your client has become overly ritualistic when it comes to their diet," adds Stokes. "If you find out it takes them an extraordinary amount of time to shop for food, that could be another indicator."

Like other eating disorders, orthorexia may also have a lot to do with control. Those with orthorexia often want to be able to heavily regulate the health food they consume. Kronberg says this may be particularly true of clients who have an unmanageable illness and have become desperate to take control of their situation.

42   ISSUE 3 / Can an Overemphasis on Eating Healthy Become . . . ?

"If they have some illness or disease that medicine could not cure, they may become obsessed with their diet, something they feel they can control even when they can't control the disease," she explains. "Maybe they have cancer and they follow a macrobiotic diet extremely rigidly. Or maybe they have multiple sclerosis and they read a book that said to eliminate animal protein. These behaviors can start with good intentions but can lead to a restrictive diet, which isn't healthy for the client."

But a person's desire to gain control doesn't have to be the result of an illness. Orthorexia may stem from someone hearing about a negative effect of a food type or group and ultimately eliminating it from his or her diet. Fat is a good example, says Stokes.

"Some people may have this intense fear that fat is bad and will kill them, so they avoid it at all costs," he says. "But in fact, fat can be healthy, particularly unsaturated fats, [which] may actually be able to protect our heart and lower our cholesterol. We don't need much fat, but we do need some. It's important for the health of our skin and our hair. And we also have fat deposits throughout sensitive places in the body, such as on the temples to protect the skull from impact or around the kidneys to provide some cushioning" should someone fall.

Some with orthorexia are focused more on what they do eat than on what they don't. This could mean, for instance, eating only organic foods. But in many cases, orthorexic tendencies may drive a person to eliminate those foods that he or she believes to be bad—commonly carbohydrates, trans fats, animal products, dyes, and sugars. Doing so can ultimately lead to malnutrition.

A recent article on orthorexia that appeared in **The New York Times** reported on an 18-year-old girl who began her struggle with food when she started eliminating all carbohydrates, meats, refined sugars, and processed foods from her diet. By the time she had gotten rid of all of the foods that she thought were not "pure," she had brought her daily calorie intake down to only 500. Her weight fell to 68 lbs, and she was repeatedly hospitalized until she finally received help and restored her weight. Which food(s) your client may obsess over depends largely on his or her own experiences. "It's all based on information," says Kronberg. "People may have become carb restrictive because of the Atkins diet or fat phobic because of some various theories they've heard. It's all about what they read or what they hear, and the obsession differs from person to person."

How to Help

Dietitians who specialize in eating disorders are most likely the best match for someone dealing with orthorexia. However, all dietitians can learn to recognize early signs and perhaps even prevent orthorexic tendencies from developing. "In general, dietitians need to take the leading role in helping patients to 'legalize' all foods by educating about the nutritional value of all foods, as well as teaching mindful eating techniques and empowering individuals to use primarily internal cues when making eating decisions," says Kauffmann.

Tribole adds that it's important for dietitians to be careful that they do not generate or enable a client's fear of certain foods or food types. While the average person may take advice about avoiding trans fats and apply it meaningfully to the diet, an individual who is bordering on developing an eating disorder may distort that information. "You may be giving out very ordinary nutritional advice, but if they have an eating disorder brewing and you don't know it, then it could be taken the wrong way," says Tribole. "It's just important to pay attention to the way we give out orders to our clients."

"Dietitians can end up being an ally to the disorder without even recognizing it," agrees Kronberg. "Clients could come to you seeking assistance for their disorder, ways that they can be more obsessively healthy. It's our job to recognize when it's become a problem and balance things back out."

Orthorexia may be an emerging condition, but dietitians should realize that they have the power to prevent it from becoming a more widespread issue. Kronberg notes, "We're on the front line, so it's crucial that we're able to recognize early on when there's a problem."

Chris Woolston  **NO**

What's Wrong With the American Diet?

What's wrong with the typical American diet? This is what the experts have to say:

"Too many calories," says Marion Nestle, PhD, MPH, Professor of Nutrition and Food Studies at New York University.

"Too many calories," asserts Melanie Polk, registered dietitian and former director of nutrition education for the American Institute of Cancer Research.

Barbara Gollman, a registered dietitian who used to be the spokesperson for the American Dietetic Association, weighs in with her own theory: "Too many calories."

Perhaps it's time to stop talking about fatty foods and admit that we simply eat too many calories. Twenty-five years ago, the average American consumed about 1,850 calories each day. Since then, our daily diet has grown by 304 calories (roughly the equivalent of two cans of soda). That's theoretically enough to add an extra 31 pounds to each person every year. Judging from the ongoing obesity epidemic, many Americans are gaining those pounds—and then some.

Take the latest national surveys on weight. More than sixty-six percent of all Americans are considered overweight, according to the Centers for Disease Control and Prevention. (This means they have a Body Mass Index greater than 25.)

But calories don't tell the whole story. To truly understand what's wrong with the American diet, you have to know how we manage to consume all those calories. There are two possible ways to go overboard: You can eat too many calorie-dense foods, or you can eat too much food or beverages in general. Many people choose to do both.

Our fondness for fast food is taking a particularly heavy toll. Although the federal government recommends that we have at least two to five cups of fruits and vegetables a day, for example, surveys show that the average American eats only three servings a day, and 42 percent eat fewer than two servings a day.

Here's a closer look at our love affair with calories—and the health crisis it has created.

The Carnival Mirror

Of course, there is no single American diet. We all have our individual tastes, quirks, and habits. Still, experts see clear patterns in our food choices. In fact, most American diets fall into one of two broad categories: "Western" or "prudent."

The prudent diet is a nutritionist's dream. People in this category tend to eat relatively large amounts of fish, poultry, cruciferous vegetables (i.e. cabbage and broccoli), greens, tomatoes, legumes, fresh fruits, and whole grains. They also skimp on fatty or calorie-rich foods such as red meats, eggs, high-fat dairy products, french fries, pizza, mayonnaise, candy, and desserts.

The Western diet is the prudent diet reflected in a carnival mirror. Everything is backwards: Red meat and other fatty foods take the forefront, while fruits, vegetables, and whole grains are pushed aside. In addition to fat and calories, the Western diet is loaded with cholesterol, salt, and sugar. If that weren't bad enough, it's critically short on dietary fiber and many nutrients—as well as plant-based substances (phytochemicals) that help protect the heart and ward off cancer.

Put it all together and you have a recipe for disaster. In a 12-year study of more than 69,000 women, published in the *Archives of Internal Medicine,* a Western diet was found to significantly raise the risk of coronary heart disease. Other studies have shown that a high-fat, low-nutrient diet increases the likelihood of colon cancer, diabetes, and a host of other ailments.

Portion Distortion

The Western diet is nothing new. The typical American family in the 1950s was more likely than we are to sit down to a meal of pork chops and mashed potatoes than stir-fried tofu and broccoli. So why has the obesity epidemic exploded in the last 20 years? It's a matter of size. "Twenty years ago, the diet wasn't as varied as it is today, and people didn't eat nearly enough fruits and vegetables," Gollman says. "But the portions were more in line with what people really need."

From bagel shops to family restaurants to vending machines to movie theater concession stands to the dining room table, our meals and snacks are taking on gargantuan proportions. "Everyone in the food industry decided they had to make portions larger to stay competitive, and people got used to large sizes very quickly," Nestle says. "Today, normal sizes seem skimpy."

The hyperinflation of our diet is especially obvious away from home. "Look through the window of any of the big chain restaurants, and you'll see huge platters of food coming out of the kitchen," Polk says. One of those platters could easily pack 2,000 calories, enough to last most people all day.

Convenience Culture

Despite our national obsession with weight loss, the obesity epidemic continues to be a national health concern. The human craving for fats and sweets will never go away, and it's getting easier than ever to satisfy those cravings. With 170,000 fast-food restaurants and 3 million soft-drink vending machines spread across the country, huge doses of calories are never far away—especially when those soda machines are sitting right in the middle of public schools.

In 1978, for example, the typical teen-age boy in the United States drank about seven ounces of soda a day, according to *Fast Food Nation* author Eric Schlosser. Today, he drinks nearly three times that much, getting a whopping 9 percent of his daily calories from soda. Teenage girls are close behind.

Perhaps not surprisingly, studies show that childhood obesity has hit epidemic proportions over the last decade. One study, published in the *Journal of the American Medical Association,* notes that from 1986 to 1998 the number of overweight white children doubled. Among Latino and African American kids, there's a 120 percent increase. More recent data shows no significant changes in the past few years, though the number of overweight kids remains high. The main culprits, according to experts: high-fat foods, sodas, and too little exercise.

However, the obesity epidemic has moved some to take action. In 2006, the Alliance for a Healthier Generation struck a deal with the American Beverage Association to eliminate high-calorie soft drinks from public schools by the 2009–2010 academic year. While government agencies and private industry grapple with implementing new policies, ultimately it will be up to us individually to improve the way we eat and increase the amount of exercise we get.

Taking Control

Fatty, unbalanced, and oversized: That, in a nutshell, is the American diet. But it doesn't have to be your diet. "People think eating healthy is a difficult task, but small things make a big difference," Polk says. "You just have to employ some important strategies. It's called taking charge."

If you eat more than four meals away from home each week, you can start by making healthy choices as you dine. "As we eat at restaurants more and more, we have to take control of these outlandish meals," Polk says. Order foods that have been baked, steamed, or grilled instead of deep-fried. Have your salad dressing or other fatty toppings served on the side, and if mayonnaise isn't low-fat, skip it entirely. Consider ordering a salad and an appetizer instead of an entree. If you do order an entree, plan to take at least half of it home with you. For more information on portion control, see Downsize This!. ["Downsize This: The Fun of Smaller Portions" by Chris Woolston (updated on Sept. 18, 2009) is available at: http://www.cvshealthresources.com/topic/portions]

No matter where you eat, try to stick to a few basic guidelines. The amount you should eat depends on your age and activity level—teenage boys and men need to eat more than young children, for example. Aim for three to eight ounces of bread, cereal, rice, or pasta each day, the more whole grains the better. This isn't quite as daunting as it sounds—one cup of rice counts as two ounces, and a single slice of bread counts as one ounce. Two to five cups of fruits and vegetables each day will give you fiber and vital nutrients. (One serving is a medium piece of fruit, a half cup of chopped fruit, a half cup of chopped vegetables, or a cup of fresh greens.) Taken together, fruits, vegetables, and grains can satisfy your hunger and fuel your body without blowing your calorie budget.

Meat isn't forbidden, but try to think of it as a complement to your meals, not the main attraction. According to the U.S. Department of Agriculture (USDA) food pyramid, you only need two servings (up to six and a half ounces) from the "meat group" each day. The group includes meat, poultry, fish, dry beans, eggs, and nuts. It goes without saying that six ounces of salmon, pinto beans, or chicken breast is preferable to six ounces of marbled steak (a serving of meat, by the way, should be about the size of a deck of cards).

NO / Chris Woolston   **47**

Much of the advice can be boiled down to one word: moderation. By eating different foods from every part of the pyramid and watching your portion size, you can make your own personal American diet healthy and nutritious. We have more choices and more temptations than ever before, but ultimately, we also have the final say over what we eat. Take control, and enjoy.

CHALLENGE QUESTIONS

Can an Overemphasis on Eating Healthy Become Unhealthy?

1. List eating habits of a person with orthorexia.
2. Compare a person with orthorexia nervosa to one with anorexia nervosa.
3. Outline the nutrition messages from USDA, professional health associations such as AMA and ADA, and registered dietitians as related to healthy eating.
4. Do you think the dietary messages and advice to "eat right" that *many* nutrition experts and government agencies encourage may cause orthorexia? Explain your answer.
5. Currently, the APA does not include orthorexia nervosa as a clinical mental disorder in their DSM. Why do you think it is not currently in their manual? Do you think it should be considered a clinical mental disorder. Explain your answer.

Internet References . . .

The General Accounting Office (GAO)

In response to congressional requests, General Accounting Office (GAO) investigators produce reports on many issues related to agriculture, food, nutrition, and health. They also testify before Congress on these issues. This site provides the full text of GAO reports and testimony.

http://www.gao.gov

The American Diabetes Association

The American Diabetes Association promotes research, education, and advocacy to prevent, cure, and treat people with diabetes mellitus, type 1 ("juvenile-onset") and type 2 ("adult-onset"). This site provides information about these conditions for health professionals and the public. It also provides access to the association's journals, many of which publish articles on aspects of diet and diabetes prevention and control, such as the glycemic index.

http://www.diabetes.org/homepage.jsp